CONTENTS

Book 3.1

UNIT 1: GREAT ADVENTURES

Book 3.1

UNIT 2: NATURE LINKS

Book 3.1

UNIT 3: BE CREATIVE!

Book 3.2

UNIT 1: TELL ME MORE

Book 3.2

UNIT 2: THINK IT THROUGH

Book 3.2

UNIT 3: TURNING POINTS

Name______________________________ Date______________ **Practice 1**

Story Elements

The **setting** is where and when a story takes place. The **characters** are the people the story is about.

Read the story. Then answer each question.

My name is Dawn. I live on a farm in New Jersey. Our farm has hills with apple trees. Every fall, the apples on our trees are ready to be picked.

Every fall, Grandmother María comes from Texas to visit us. Together, we make apple juice and apple pies. She tells me stories. My favorite stories are about my father when he was a boy.

"When your father was the same age as you, he rode horses," Grandmother María said.

"Where did he ride?" I asked.

"All over our ranch," Grandmother María said.

Then she told me that Texas was so big that a boy could ride all day and never see a house or a person. She said that instead of apple trees, my father saw cactus plants.

1. Where does Dawn live? ____________________________
2. Where is the farm? ____________________________
3. When does Dawn pick apples? ____________________________
4. Who are the three characters in the story? ____________________________

   ____
5. Who is Grandmother María's story about? ____________________________

   ____
6. Where is Grandmother María's story set? ____________________________

At Home: Have students make up a story about someone visiting them. Have them identify their story's characters and settings.

Name____________________ Date__________ **Practice 2**

Vocabulary

Supply the correct words from the list.

scattered enormous towering journey surrounded astonished

The long __________ to the center of the desert was well worth it. Everything we saw there __________ us. It was all so different!

Wonders of nature __________ our campsite in every direction. There were __________ sand drifts that seemed to sweep across the desert floor like huge tidal waves. Overhead were __________ cliffs made of red and black sandstone.

The most amazing thing we saw was the tumbleweed __________ about the desert for miles and miles. Strong, warm winds whipped them into action. We marveled as they danced across the horizon.

At Home: Have students read the dictionary definitions for each of the vocabulary words.

The Dream

I always remember my dreams. Usually they are about a *journey*. In last night's dream my journey was very strange. It *astonished* and amazed me.

In my dream, my bed was as *enormous* as a swimming pool. While I was in it, it rolled out of the house and onto the sidewalk. On the sidewalk there were many toys *scattered* under tall, *towering* trees.

I stopped my huge bed from rolling by grabbing one of the trees. Then I climbed down a giant ladder to get off my bed. On the ground, I was *surrounded* by the greatest toys I had ever seen in my life. What a dream!

1. How did the author feel about the dream?

____

2. What types of dreams does the author best remember?

____

3. What things are *scattered* in the dream?

____

4. What two words describe the size of things in this dream?

____

5. Why might the dreamer have been happy the bed rolled outside?

____

At Home: Have students draw a picture of two things at home that are enormous.

Name______________________________ Date____________ **Practice 3**

Story Comprehension

Read each statement. Write **T** if the statement describes "Grandfather's Journey." Write **F** if the statement does not correctly describe "Grandfather's Journey."

1. _____ The grandfather first left Japan when he was an old man.
2. _____ Grandfather traveled to North America on his journey.
3. _____ Grandfather saw the desert on his trip to the New World.
4. _____ The grandfather explored North America by covered wagon.
5. _____ For part of his journey, Grandfather traveled by steamship.
6. _____ The grandfather liked Florida best.
7. _____ Grandfather returned to Japan to get married and because he was homesick.
8. _____ The grandson went to California because his grandfather had told him stories about the place.
9. _____ The grandfather, his new wife, and baby daughter lived in San Francisco.
10. _____ The grandson now lives in China.

At Home: Have students imagine a faraway place that they would like to visit. Have them write down reasons why they would like to go and things they would expect to find there.

/10

Name____________________ Date__________ **Practice 4**

Use Book Parts

The **author** and the **title** of a book appear on both the front cover and the side of the book, or **spine**.

Old Friends	Joe Parker
Victorian Porches	Selma Davidson
Painting Easter Eggs	Paula Brunst
COMPUTER REPAIR	Kathy Verang
Wigs and Hats	Rhonda Newcomb

Cooking with Woks	Li Woo
Kindergarten Art	Harry Waters
JUMP ROPE	Rhonda Newcomb
Bonsai Trees	Larry Larsen
Scary Stories	Paula Arnot

Use the stacks of books to answer these questions.

1. Who wrote a book about art in kindergarten? __________
2. What is the title of the book written by Joe Parker? __________
3. If your computer was broken, which book would you need? __________

   ____
4. Who wrote more than one book in these piles? __________
5. What is the title of the book about cooking? __________
6. Who wrote Scary Stories? __________
7. What is the name of the book that Larry Larsen wrote? __________
8. Which book did Paula Brunst write? __________

At Home: Ask students which book they would look in to find information about miniature trees.

Name____________________ Date__________ **Practice 5**

Story Elements

Grandfather is the main **character** in "Grandfather's Journey." Japan and North America are the **settings**, or places where the story happens. Answer the questions about the main character and settings in the chart below.

CHARACTER:	**SETTINGS:**
Grandfather	**North America**
1. Why does Grandfather leave Japan? ________________	4. What does Grandfather like best about California? ________________
	Japan
2. What does Grandfather like best when he returns to Japan? ________________	5. Why does Grandfather decide not to build a house in his village? ________________
3. What does Grandfather tell his grandson stories about? Why? ________________	6. Why does Grandfather spend the end of his life in his village? ________________

At Home: Have students make a drawing for one story setting. Write a sentence that describes the drawing.

Name________________________ Date____________ **Practice 6**

Make Predictions

You can use what you have learned about a character in a story to **predict** what this character might do. Read each story. Then answer the questions.

Tanisha is good at solving problems. She also likes taking care of her little brother. Last summer, Tanisha and her family went on a camping trip. One afternoon, Tanisha and her little brother got lost on the way from their tent to the car. Tanisha's brother became scared and started to cry.

1. Will the children find their way back to the tent? How do you know?

____

Tonight, Jerry has to finish a science project for school. Tomorrow is the science fair. They are giving prizes for the best project. Jerry would really like to win a prize. Tonight, Jerry's favorite TV show is on from eight o'clock to eight-thirty. Jerry has to go to bed at eight-thirty.

2. Will Jerry finish his science project? Why?

____

3. When will Jerry work on his science project? ____________________

____

Wendy lives in the country. The ocean is far away. Her favorite books are about boats. She dreams of sailing far and fast across the ocean.

Last summer, Wendy's father asked her to choose what they would do on their next summer trip.

4. What will Wendy and her father do on their next summer trip?

____

At Home: Have students pick a character from a movie. Ask students to describe what the character is like and predict something that the character might do.

Name______________________________ Date____________ **Practice 7**

Compound Words

A **compound word** is a word that is made up of two smaller words. Each word in a compound word can stand alone.

brake + man = brakeman

Use the picture clues to write the compound word. The first part of the compound word appears below.

		First Word	Compound Word
1.		basket	____________
2.		rail	____________
3.		home	____________
4.		camp	____________
5.		jelly	____________

At Home: Ask students to tell you three more examples of compound words.

Name________________________ Date____________ **Practice 8**

Problem and Solution

The answer you find to a **problem** is called the **solution**.

Draw a line between the problem and its matching solution.

Problem	Solution
1. There is a lot of snow on the ground.	**a.** My mother will bring the bike to a bike shop.
2. My baby sister was crying.	**b.** My dad bought a big umbrella for us to sit under.
3. My bike has a flat tire.	**c.** I wear my boots to school.
4. Our babysitter is on a trip, and my parents are going out on Friday night.	**d.** Mom helps me get dressed in the morning.
5. My dad has no time to paint the house.	**e.** We replaced the glass.
6. We can't sit in our backyard because it's too hot.	**f.** I rocked the baby to sleep.
7. I broke my arm, and I can't button my shirt.	**g.** My grandparents offer to spend the weekend.
8. My brother broke a window.	**h.** He hires a painter.

At Home: Have students write another problem and solution pair.

Name____________________ Date__________ **Practice 9**

Vocabulary

Write a vocabulary word from the list that means almost the same thing as the underlined words.

legend correct groaning unusual continue embarrass

1. Do you think an octopus is a strange and ____________ animal?
2. We were right, she gave us the ____________ answer.
3. Spilling milk in front of twenty people might shame or ____________ you.
4. A ____________ and a folk tale are similar kinds of stories.
5. The bear held its injured paw and started moaning and ____________ in pain.
6. Keep going, ____________ to the next green light.

At Home: Have students create a crossword puzzle using the vocabulary words.

Eric and the Happy Answer

Once there was a boy named Eric. Eric liked to be *correct*. If his teacher said he was doing something the wrong way, Eric would still *continue*. "I would *embarrass* myself if I said I had been wrong," he thought.

One day Eric's teacher heard him *groaning* at his desk. "Why are you making such an *unusual* sound?" she asked. "You sound like a strange creature in a *legend* or tall tale."

"I don't want to think I'm always right," Eric said. "Next time I'm doing something wrong will you help me do it right?"

"Of course!" the teacher replied.

From that day on, things changed for Eric.

1. Who always thought he had to be *correct*?

 ____

2. What was Eric afraid he would do if he said he was wrong?

 ____

3. What *unusual* thing did his teacher hear Eric doing?

 ____

4. What did Eric sound like when he was *groaning*?

 ____

5. Why did things change for Eric?

 ____

At Home: Have students write about a time they asked for help. Were they afraid to ask? Were they happy they did?

Name________________________ Date____________ **Practice 10**

Story Comprehension

Answer the questions about "Phoebe and the Spelling Bee."

1. Why is Phoebe afraid of Friday? ______________________________

____

____

2. Why does Phoebe pretend to be sick at school? ______________________________

____

____

3. How is Katie different from her friend Phoebe? ______________________________

____

____

4. How does Phoebe upset Katie? ______________________________

____

____

5. How does Phoebe make up for what she does to Katie? ______________________________

____

____

6. Why do Phoebe and Katie get certificates? ______________________________

____

____

At Home: Have students choose a word they find difficult to spell. Then have them make a sign that gives a spelling tip for that word. Post the signs in a place where everyone can see them.

Name________________________________ Date______________ **Practice 11**

Use a Glossary

A **glossary** is a list of words and definitions for a specific book.

124 Shetland pony–Stomp

Shetland pony (noun) 1. a small-built pony of a breed that came from the Shetland Islands
shortchange (verb) 1. to give less money back than is owed 2. to cheat or trick
shoe (noun) 1. a covering for the foot 2. a piece of metal for a horse's foot
slouch (verb) 1. to sit with an awkward, drooping posture
snake oil (noun) 1. a worthless preparation sold as medicine
sofa bed (noun) 1. a couch that unfolds into a bed
son (noun) 1. a male child
springer spaniel (noun) 1. a dog having drooping ears and a silky brown and white coat
stomachache (noun) 1. a pain in the belly

Use the part of a glossary page above to answer these questions.

1. Is *stomachache* a noun, verb, adverb, or adjective? ____________
2. What word comes after *shoe* in this glossary? ______________________
3. To find the definition of the word *stories*, would you look before or after this page in the glossary? Explain. ____________________________

   ____
4. What are the guide words for the page on which *son* appears?

   ____
5. Pretend you saw the word *shoe* in a story about an animal who can't walk because of sore feet. Which of the two definitions shown in the glossary would apply? Write that definition. ______________________

   ____

At Home: Ask students to think of another word that would fall between the guide words on this glossary page.

Name________________________ Date____________ **Practice 12**

Problem and Solution

One subject in school presents **problems** for the main character in "Phoebe and the Spelling Bee." Read each problem in the chart below. Then write the solution Phoebe finds for the problem.

Problem	Solution
1. Phoebe needs to learn how to spell **actor** correctly.	1. ________________
2. On Tuesday, Mrs. Ravioli asks Phoebe if she's looked at the spelling list yet. Phoebe has not spent a lot of time on spelling.	2. ________________
3. Mrs. Ravioli gives a practice spelling bee, and Phoebe is not ready for it.	3. ________________
4. Katie is mad at Phoebe for lying to her.	4. ________________
5. Phoebe wants to learn how to spell the word **method**.	5. ________________
6. Phoebe misspells the word **brontosaurus**.	6. ________________

At Home: Have students use Pheobe's spelling techniques. Have them write stories to help them remember this week's spelling words.

Name________________________ Date______________ **Practice 13**

Make Predictions

What you learn in a story can help you **predict** what will happen next. Read each story. Then answer the questions.

Mrs. Miller is ninety years old. She lives alone in a small house. Three children live next door to Mrs. Miller. Every Saturday they visit her. Sometimes they help her do things around the house. Lately, Mrs. Miller has been feeling a little tired. She has not been able to rake the leaves or weed her garden.

1. What might happen the next time the children visit Mrs. Miller?

____

2. What parts of the story helped you make your prediction? ________

____

____

Elaine and Michael found soda cans all over the sidewalk. They thought the cans made the street look messy. So they began collecting the cans. Elaine's father told the children about a new store down the block that bought soda cans for a nickel each.

3. What do you think might happen next in the story? ________

____

____

4. What parts of the story helped you make your prediction? ________

____

____

At Home: The next time students begin a TV program or a book, ask them to predict an outcome. Have them write down their prediction, and then check it when they find out the outcome.

Name________________________________ Date______________ **Practice 14**

Prefixes

A **prefix** is a word part that can be added to the beginning of a word. It creates a new word with its own meaning. The prefix **un-** means "not," or "opposite of." For example, the word **unfair** means "not fair" or "the opposite of fair."

Below each sentence, write the word that includes the prefix **un-**. Then write the meaning of the word.

1. It was unlucky that Mona was sick on the first day of vacation.

   ____

2. The story has an unusual character named Simon.

   ____

3. The movie was very interesting, even though it was untrue.

   ____

4. It took the child a long time to unwrap her birthday present.

   ____

5. The number of stars in the sky is unknown.

   ____

6. Jack was unhappy that he did not get a better score in the game.

   ____

At Home: Ask students to name three other words that begin with the prefix **un-**.

Name________________________________ Date______________ **Practice 15**

Steps in a Process

A series of steps you follow in order are called **steps in a process**.

The steps below in each set are not in order. Write numbers 1 through 4 on the lines to show the order.

Shop for Spaghetti

_____ Put noodles in shopping cart.

_____ Go to the store.

_____ Choose a shopping cart.

_____ Pay for the noodles.

Go Skating with a Friend

_____ Skate down the street together.

_____ Find skates in closet.

_____ Put on right and left skates.

_____ Skate to friend's house.

Cook Spaghetti

_____ Put the cooked noodles on a plate.

_____ Go to the kitchen.

_____ Open the box of noodles.

_____ Cook the noodles in a pan.

Go to School

_____ Walk out the door.

_____ Pick up the school books.

_____ Wake up on time.

_____ Get dressed.

At Home: Help students to identify a step-by-step process that they follow at home. Have them write down the steps in order.

Name________________________ Date____________ **Practice 16**

Vocabulary

Supply the correct words from the list:

length guard royal within gift straighten

Once a prince and a princess lived happily in an underground castle. There was one problem, though. The ________________ kingdom always looked boring and dull. So the prince had an idea. As a birthday ________________ he bought the princess some paintings to decorate the castle walls.

The princess was thrilled! Her favorite painting showed a small face tucked ________________ a larger face. She hung this one on the castle door, next to the ________________ who protected them. Another painting showed a group of bent and slanted lines. If you looked at the lines long enough, they seemed to ________________ out. Looking at this will keep people busy, she thought.

After three days all of the paintings were hung, except one. This last painting is shown below. Do you think the lines are the same

________________?

At Home: Use each of the vocabulary words in a sentence.

Anything Can Happen!

I used to visit the land of make-believe very often. *Within* the land of make-believe, anything can happen! Once, an old woman offered me a ring as a *gift*. The ring changed shape as fast as I could say "one, two, three." Then I made it *straighten* out into a long magic wand.

With my magic wand I knew I could become anyone and anything I wished. I decided to become a *guard* for a *royal* family. I marched up and down the *length* of their long hallway. Then I marched right into the royal kitchen. You can find all kinds of cookies and cakes in the land of make-believe!

1. What kind of family lived in the castle?

____

2. What did the speaker have to do to change the ring to a wand?

____

3. What kind of person watches over *royal* families?

____

4. When you measure from one end to the other of the castle hall, what do you learn?

____

5. What is special about the land of make-believe?

____

At Home: Encourage students to write about what they would like to find within the world of make-believe.

Name____________________ Date____________ **Practice 17**

Story Comprehension

Review the optical illusions shown in “Opt.” Then list two of the illusions under each heading.

What Colors Do You See?	How Many Objects?
1. ________________	3. ________________
2. ________________	4. ________________
The Same Size?	**Hidden Faces?**
5. ________________	7. ________________
6. ________________	8. ________________
Straight or Crooked?	**Changing Shapes?**
9. ________________	11. ________________
10. ________________	12. ________________

At Home: Ask students to circle the two optical illusions that they enjoyed the most.

Name______________________ Date__________ **Practice 18**

Use a Table of Contents

Use the headings below to fill in two tables of contents. Notice that one table of contents is for a book of fiction, that is, a made-up story. The other is for a nonfiction book, which is about real things.

Nailing the Box Together 17	Meteorite Science Project 12
by Claire Rollins	Snacks From Saturn 31
Clearing the Ground 2	Harvesting Your Crop 53

Name________________________ Date______________ Practice 19

Steps in a Process

Think about the steps you use when you solve a problem. Often you can use the same steps to solve other problems. Writing down the steps will help you remember them. A series of steps you follow in order are called **steps in a process**.

Read Problem 1 and the list of steps for solving it below. Then write a list of steps for solving Problem 2.

Problem 1

What steps will help you find out if the vertical lines of the messenger's cloak are crooked or straight?

Process

1. Measure the distance between two lines near the top.
2. Write down that number.
3. Measure the distance between the same two lines near the bottom.
4. Write down this number.
5. Compare your two measurements. If they are the same, the lines are straight.

Problem 2

In the picture of the Royal Pet at the zoo, what steps will help you decide if the body of the pet is shorter than its neck?

Process

1. ____________________
2. ____________________
3. ____________________
4. ____________________
5. ____________________

____

At Home: Have students follow the steps they wrote. What did they discover about the length of the Royal Pet's neck and body? Have them record the results.

Name________________________ Date____________ **Practice 20**

Story Elements

The **narrator** tells the story. Often, the narrator is one of the **characters**, or people in the story. The narrator tells the story from his or her own **point of view.**

Read each part of the story below. Then answer the questions about it.

The queen called me. I was on the other side of the room. "Princess Lulu," the queen said. "How long will it take you to get from there to here?"

1. Who are the two main characters? ____________________

2. What two words tell you that Princess Lulu is the narrator? ________

____

My brother, Randy, told me a funny story. I have never laughed so hard in all my life! My brother is such a clown! He says he's glad I am his sister.

3. Who are the main characters? ____________________

4. Who is the narrator? What words help you to know this? ________

____

The dog's name is Toaster. The brown spots on his white fur are shaped like pieces of toast. Ernie is Toaster's owner. Ernie named his dog Toaster.

5. Who are the two main characters? ____________________

6. Is the narrator one of the two main characters? How do you know?

____

____

At Home: Have students narrate a story. Then have them try to tell their stories from a different point of view.

Prefixes

You can add the **prefixes un-** or **dis-** to the beginnings of some words to make new words. The prefix **un-** means "opposite of" or "not." The prefix **dis-** also means "opposite of" or "not."

Rewrite each sentence. Replace the underlined phrase with a word from the box that includes the prefix **un-** or **dis-**. Look at the following example:

Sean was <u>not lucky</u> flying the kite.

Sean was **un**lucky flying the kite.

unusual	unknown	displeased	disobeyed	unbelievable

1. The stranger was <u>not known</u> to the family.

   ____

2. Jeri <u>did not please</u> her science teacher.

   ____

3. Quong's painting was <u>not the same as everyone else's.</u>

   ____

4. My little brother can yell so loud it is <u>not believable.</u>

   ____

5. Bruce <u>did not obey</u> the rule.

   ____

Name________________________ Date______________ **Practice 22**

Problem and Solution

Characters in stories often face **problems**. The answers to their problems are called **solutions**. Read the problems below. Then complete the chart by writing down two ways to solve each problem.

Problem	Solutions
Your class is going to write letters to pen pals. Everyone's pencil point is broken and there is no sharpener. What can the class do?	1. ______________________ ______________________ 2. ______________________ ______________________
A vacant lot across the street from your school is covered with rocks. Nobody likes looking at the lot. What can your school do?	3. ______________________ ______________________ 4. ______________________ ______________________
It is your friend's birthday. You forgot to buy a present. What can you do?	5. ______________________ ______________________ 6. ______________________ ______________________

At Home: Help students to identify problems in their neighborhoods. Brainstorm together to find some solutions.

Name ______________________ Date ______________ **Practice 23**

Vocabulary

Supply the correct words from the list.

scene ceiling eager including section cents

Juliana was ________________ to see the new house. She couldn't wait! There was even a picture of a carnival painted in her new bedroom. "It's on the ________________," her father had said. "You'll be able to see it as you lie in bed." Juliana thought a carnival was a great ________________ to watch before falling asleep.

There was another thing that Juliana liked about her new house. Even ________________ a ten-minute bus ride, the house was still closer to school.

Juliana's mother bought her a new book bag for the daily trip. It was a present to celebrate their moving. The bag cost seven dollars and eighty ________________. They found it in the sports ________________ of the department store.

"Of all places!" Juliana's mother exclaimed as she picked up the bag. "You never know where you'll find things!"

At Home: Have students use each vocabulary word in a sentence.

Tanya's Books

Tanya ran out of books to read. So one day she decided to write her own book. She was *eager* to start. "It will have neat stuff, *including* pictures," she said.

Tanya's mother gave Tanya ninety *cents* to buy a new pen. Then Tanya began to write. Her story was about a house where the *ceiling* became the floor. In one *scene*, the family in the house tried to eat breakfast upside down.

The story was so funny, Tanya decided to write a longer story. This second story had five sections. Each *section* told about a friend of hers.

When Tanya finished her second story she gave each of her friends a copy. Everyone liked it.

1. What did Tanya do when she ran out of books to read?

____

2. What does the floor become in Tanya's first book?

____

3. What word tells how Tanya feels about writing her books?

____

4. What word describes one setting and event in Tanya's first book?

____

5. How much money did Tanya's mother give her?

____

5

At Home: Encourage students to talk about what kind of story they would write if they ran out of books to read.

Name ____________________ Date __________ **Practice 24**

Story Comprehension

Look back over "Max Malone." Then complete the chart below.

1. Setting of story	________________ ________________
2. Main characters	________________
3. Beginning of story	________________ ________________
4. Middle of story	________________ ________________ ________________ ________________
5. End of Story	________________ ________________

Now match each detail.

6. _____ sells all the baseballs for $5 — **a.** Dusty Field

7. _____ had his appendix taken out — **b.** Max

8. _____ a baseball player — **c.** Toys are Less

9. _____ gets idea to buy baseballs for $5 — **d.** Gordy

10. _____ helps Max sell the baseballs — **e.** Austin

At Home: Have students think of some ways to make money similar to the way Max and Gordy did.

Name______________________________ Date____________ **Practice 25**

Use an Index

An **index** can help you find information in a nonfiction book. The numbers for pages with illustrations are set in italics.

622 – **Index**

1. On what page would you find information on Native American money?

____

2. Where would facts about money systems be found?

____

3. Besides page 202, where else would you read about shells being used as Pacific Island money? ____________________

4. If you wanted to know how paper money is printed in the United States, would this page of the index help you to find out? ______________

5. Which page probably has an illustration of a financial magazine? ____

6. On which pages would you find information about the failure of mutual funds? ____________

At Home: Ask students what they think is the overall topic for the book of which the index above is a part.

Name________________________ Date______________ **Practice 26**

Problem and Solution

You can often find **solutions,** or answers, to even the most difficult **problems.** Finish the chart by writing down how Max and Gordy solved each of their problems.

Problem	Solution
1. Max and Gordy have $2.50 each and want to buy as many 20¢ baseballs as they can.	
2. Max and Gordy feel shy about selling their baseballs to people at the sporting-goods store.	
3. Max and Gordy both want their own Dusty Field-autographed baseballs.	
4. Max and Gordy forget to save a baseball for Austin.	
5. Max and Gordy know that Austin is sad about not seeing Dusty Field.	

At Home: Have the students think of problems they might have if they were home sick from school. Then have them write down ways that friends could help them.

Name________________________ Date______________ **Practice 27**

Story Elements

A **plot** is what happens in a story. The **characters** are who the story is about. Read the story before you answer each question.

Tippy was a small brown dog. Fluffy was a black cat with long hair. Both animals lived with their owner, Lisa. One day Lisa let her pets out into the backyard. Both animals wanted to see something new. Right away, Fluffy jumped over the fence. Tippy dug a hole under the fence and crawled through.

Fluffy and Tippy happily ran from yard to yard. Suddenly a big dog appeared. It was the largest, scariest dog Fluffy and Tippy had ever seen. The dog barked and growled. Fluffy and Tippy turned around and ran straight back to their yard.

1. Who are the main characters? ______________________________

____

2. What do the main characters want to do? ______________________

____

3. How are the characters able to do this? ______________________

____

4. What problem do Tippy and Fluffy run into? ___________________

____

5. What do the animals do next? _______________________________

____

6. Do you think the animals learned anything from their experience?

____

At Home: Have students draw pictures of other things that could have happened in the story.

Name________________ Date__________ **Practice 28**

Compound Words

A **compound word** is made by joining two smaller words. The meanings of the two smaller words can help you figure out the meaning of the compound word.

Look at each of the compound words. Write the two words that make up each compound word. Then use the meanings of the two smaller words to write the meaning of the compound word.

popcorn

1. ____________ + ____________

2. meaning = ______________________________

homeland

3. ____________ + ____________

4. meaning = ______________________________

sweatshirt

5. ____________ + ____________

6. meaning = ______________________________

seacoast

7. ____________ + ____________

8. meaning = ______________________________

sandbox

9. ____________ + ____________

10. meaning = ______________________________

At Home: Ask students to name the short words in each of the following compound words: **steamship, grandfather, goldfish.**

Name________________________ Date____________ **Practice 29**

Make Predictions

Read each selection. Then make **predictions** about what might happen based on the titles and stories.

Then answer the questions to predict an outcome.

Things That Snap and Bite

Animal World is a safari park. You can drive through the park and see animals living freely, as they do in the wild. Be careful not to open your window! Some animals can be dangerous.

1. What kinds of animals do you predict live in Animal World?

____

____

2. Which parts of the story helped you make your prediction?

____

____

Rufus to the Rescue

My dog Rufus is so clever. Sometimes I think he actually understands what I am saying. Last week I got stuck climbing a tree. I shouted, "Rufus! Go home and fetch Dad!" Rufus barked at me and ran off.

3. What do you predict will happen? ______________________

____

4. Which parts of the story helped you to predict your outcome?

____

____

At Home: Have students look at a book, magazine, or newspaper. Ask them to guess what the stories are about by looking at the titles.

Name____________________ Date__________ **Practice 30**

Vocabulary

Choose the correct word from the box to complete each sentence. Then write the word on the line.

celebrated	cork	fans	pitcher	score	wrap

1. Kate ________________ her birthday by having a party.
2. A baseball's center is made out of ________________.
3. Our ________________ threw the ball for the batter to hit.
4. The ________________ cheered when David stepped onto the stage.
5. I ________________ the gift with colorful paper.
6. The goal tied the ________________ between the two teams.

Write two sentences that use two of the vocabulary words in each sentence.

7. ____

8. ____

At Home: Challenge students to write a short story about a sports event using three of the vocabulary words.

Fast Ball

Lou wanted to be a baseball player like his father. Long ago, Lou's father had been a *pitche*r on a winning team.

Pictures of Lou's father hung in Lou's bedroom. In one picture, *fans* cheered and *celebrated* as Lou's father threw the winning pitch. This pitch had made the *score* 3-0.

One afternoon, Lou went outside to practice. He wondered if he could pitch as well as his dad. It was cold, so he had to *wrap* a scarf around his neck. Then he threw the ball against a brick wall. Whack! The ball burst open and its *cork* fell out!

"Looks like I might be able to pitch", he thought. "I guess I'll give baseball a try!"

1. What is the name of the person who throws the ball to the batter?

____

2. What is inside a baseball?

____

3. What did Lou do with the scarf?

____

4. What was 3-0 in one of Lou's father's games?

____

5. What do you think Lou will do next in this story?

____

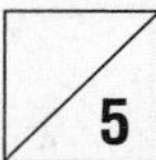

At Home: Have students talk about games and sports they like. Also encourage them to talk about any sports or games any of their family members may play.

Name ______________________ Date ____________ **Practice 31**

Story Comprehension

1. What did the Toms River Little League team do? ____________________

____

2. What was the nickname for the Toms River team? ____________________

____

3. What team did the Toms River team play against in the final game?

____

4. How long had it been since a U.S. team had won the Little League World Series? ____________________

5. What did the people of Toms River, New Jersey, do when the Little League team came home from the game? ____________________

____

____

6. What is special about Mark McGwire and Sammy Sosa? ____________________

____

7. In your own words, tell about the home run record and how it was set.

____

____

8. Is "Champions of the World" a true story? How do you know?

____

____

At Home: Have students look for pictures of people playing baseball. Then have them make a collage of pictures mixed with facts that they learned about baseball from reading "Champions of the World."

Name____________________ Date__________ **Practice 32**

Use a Search Engine

Study the make-believe Web site addresses shown below. Use them to answer the questions below.

http://www.majorleaguebaseball.com/	http://www.bigleagueslugger.com/
http://www.baseballcamps.com/	http://www.baseballscholarships.com/
http://www.tomsriver.com/	http://www.halloffame.com/

Fill in the blank with a Web site address. Pick the Web site most likely to help you.

If you wanted information about:

1. a summer camp for baseball players

   ____

2. big-league slugger baseball bats

   ____

3. the Little League World Series champs from Toms River, New Jersey

   ____

4. a sports scholarship for playing baseball in college

   ____

5. next year's complete major-league baseball schedule

   ____

6. how to visit the Hall of Fame in Cooperstown, N.Y.

   ____

At Home: Ask students what the Web site address http://www.storybooks.com might lead them to.

Name________________________ Date____________ **Practice 33**

Steps in a Process

Steps that you follow in order are called **steps in a process**. Writing down the steps in order will help you to remember them.

Think about the following activities. Each of them has several steps that need to be followed. Write down the steps in the process for each activity below.

Find a book at the library.

1. ____________________
2. ____________________
3. ____________________
4. ____________________

Make a cup of chocolate milk.

1. ____________________
2. ____________________
3. ____________________
4. ____________________
5. ____________________

Make a costume for a costume party.

1. ____________________
2. ____________________
3. ____________________
4. ____________________
5. ____________________

At Home: Have students write down five steps that they follow when they do their homework.

Name________________________ Date____________ **Practice 34**

Compound Words

You can figure out the meaning of a compound word by looking at the two smaller words within it and putting the two meanings together.

Below are definitions of some compound words. Complete the chart.

Definition	Compound Word	Two Words	
1. the town where a person makes his or her home	____________	________	________
2. balls that are used to play the game of basketball	____________	________	________
3. made at home, not at a factory or a store	____________	________	________
4. the place made for walking at the side of a road	____________	________	________
5. the days at the end of the school or work week	____________	________	________
6. case to store books	____________	________	________

At Home: Ask students to name the compound word that means **the work that you do at school.**

Name________________________ Date______________ **Practice 35**

Prefixes

A **prefix** is a word part that can be added to the beginning of a word to change the word's meaning. Knowing what a prefix means can help you figure out what a word means. The prefixes **un-** and **dis-** both mean "not" or "the opposite of."

Prefix + word	**Meaning**
dis + appears = disappears	the opposite of appears, to pass from sight
un + like = unlike	not alike, different

Write the prefix of each word. Write the word's meaning. Then use the word in a sentence of your own.

1. **disagree** Prefix: _____ Meaning: ________________________

Sentence: ____

2. **unwrapped** Prefix: _____ Meaning: ________________________

____

Sentence: ____

3. **disobey** Prefix: _____ Meaning: ________________________

Sentence: ____

4. **unlucky** Prefix: _____ Meaning: ________________________

Sentence: ____

5. **displease** Prefix: _____ Meaning: ________________________

Sentence: ____

At Home: Ask students to name three other words that begin with the prefix **dis-** and then tell you their meanings.

Unit 1 Vocabulary Review

A. Read each word in Column 1. Then find a word in Column 2 that means the opposite. Write the letter of the word on the line.

	Column 1		Column 2
_____	**1.** ceiling	**a.**	wrong
_____	**2.** enormous	**b.**	stop
_____	**3.** correct	**c.**	floor
_____	**4.** within	**d.**	tiny
_____	**5.** continue	**e.**	outside

B. Supply the correct vocabulary word.

scene	journey	celebrated	gift
fans	cents	guard	

1. The _______________ roared when Cora hit the home run.

2. Denny bought a _______________ for his grandmother.

3. The _______________ across the mountains took three days.

4. The large ball cost 75 _______________ more than the small one.

5. The class _______________ Leo's birthday by giving him a party.

6. When Jane saw the lovely _______________, she wanted to paint a picture of it.

7. Harry and Jim stood _______________ around the campfire.

At Home: Have students write a sentence for each vocabulary word in Part A.

Name____________________ Date__________ **Practice 37**

Unit 1 Vocabulary Review

A. Answer each question.

1. **royal** Who might be members of a royal family?

____

2. **wrap** Why would someone wrap a package?

____

3. **astonished** What amazing sight astonished you?

____

4. **eager** What is something you would be eager to do?

____

B. Write the vocabulary word that means almost the same as the underlined word.

section	scattered	enormous	unusual	straighten	gift

1. That kind of stone is very <u>rare</u>. ________________
2. Wally finished the first <u>part</u> of the book. ________________
3. Janet <u>spread</u> the seeds on the soil. ________________
4. Nancy will <u>fix</u> the crooked picture. ________________
5. The Statue of Liberty is <u>huge</u>. ________________
6. My friend gave me a wonderful <u>present</u>. ________________

At Home: Have students write a question for each vocabulary word in Part B. Then answer the question. Use Part A as a guide.

Cause and Effect

The person, thing or event that makes something happen is called the **cause**. The **effect** is what happens, or the result of that cause.

Read each cause. Then choose the correct effect from the box and write it on the line.

Effects

The cake got burned.

She decided to call the garage for help.

The plow trucks were busy.

She ran out of food for her guests.

The students went outside to play.

1. **Cause:** The school bell rang.

   Effect: ____

2. **Cause:** Anna's car made a lot of strange noises.

   Effect: ____

3. **Cause:** Jay fell asleep while his cake was in the oven.

   Effect: ____

4. **Cause:** More people came to Amanda's party than she expected.

   Effect: ____

5. **Cause:** It snowed for twelve hours.

   Effect: ____

At Home: Have students tell you some of the effects that could be caused by a rainy day.

Name_______________________________ Date_______________ **Practice 39**

Vocabulary

Decide whether each statement is **true** or **false**.
Explain the false statements.

1. There is still room left in a bucket that is filled *halfway*.

____

2. *Excitement* usually causes people to fall asleep.

____

3. A big pile of things is called a *heap*.

____

4. *Stems* are the part of a flower that grow out of the ground.

____

5. When a train is running on *schedule*, it is going to arrive at the station very late.

____

6. A picnic *area* is a space set aside where people can eat.

____

At Home: Have students read the dictionary definition for each of the italicized words.

Andrew's Award

The school awards show was *halfway* over. So far the program had perfectly followed the printed *schedule*. Andrew felt so much *excitement* that he paced back and forth. He was in the *area* where all the award winners waited.

Early in the school year, Andrew had collected used cans. He brought them to a place where a city worker counted them. Then the worker threw them into a big *heap* of other used cans.

Andrew received twenty dollars for the used cans. With the money, he bought flowers to plant in front of the school. By the day of the awards, the *stems* were just beginning to pop up from the ground.

1. Where did the city worker throw Andrew's cans?

____

2. What did Andrew feel at the awards show?

____

3. Where did Andrew pace back and forth?

____

4. What part of the flowers were beginning to pop up?

____

5. Why was Andrew winning an award?

____

At Home: Invite students to talk about what they would do to help their school look nice.

Name______________________________ Date____________ **Practice 40**

Story Comprehension

Think about "City Green." Then complete the chart below.

1. **Setting of the Story:** ______________________________
2. **Main Characters:** ______________________________

____

Beginning of the Story

3. ______________________________
4. ______________________________
5. ______________________________

Middle of the Story

6. ______________________________

____

7. ______________________________

____

8. ______________________________

____

End of the Story

9. ______________________________

____

10. ______________________________

____

At Home: Have students identify and discuss problems on their street or in their own community.

/10

Name______________________________ Date____________ **Practice 41**

Use a Telephone Directory

102 **Garage Doors—Gas**

Garage Doors
Clegg Brothers
45 Simpson St 555–3423
T.J.'s Garage Supplies
523 Maple Ln 555–6520
Garbage Removal
See Rubbish and Garbage Removal
Garden Centers—plants, supplies
Chestnut Hill Farms
456 Harrison Blvd .555–0456
Harry's Garden World
Route 5 + Gray Way 555–4589
Montclair Mall 555–1111
Garden Furniture
Chestnut Hill Farms
456 Harrison Blvd .555–0456
Moon River Junction
626 Good Hope Rd 555–8734

Pretend you're building a garden. Use the section of the Yellow Pages shown here to help you.

1. Which two stores sell plants? ______________________

____

2. Which store sells both both plants and garden furniture?

____

3. What's the phone number of Moon River Junction? ____________

4. Pretend you need to remove garbage from your garden. Where would you look in these Yellow Pages? ______________________

5. Which two stores sell garage doors?

____

At Home: Ask students to explain why they would not find listings of stores that sell fans on this page.

Name ______________________ Date ____________ **Practice 42**

Cause and Effect

Events in a story can often be organized by **cause** and **effect**. One event causes another to happen. Write the cause or effect of each event in the chart below.

Story Event (Cause)	Story Event (Effect)
Marcy asked Old Man Hammer about the building that used to be on the lot.	1. ______________________
Spring came.	2. ______________________
3. ______________________	Marcy and Miss Rosa dug for dirt in the empty lot. They got the idea to turn the lot into a garden.
Marcy, Miss Rosa, and other people from the block passed around a petition.	4. ______________________
5. ______________________	Everyone pitched in to help clean the lot.
6. ______________________	Marcy patted the neat and tidy garden row for good luck.
Marcy saw the tiny green shoots of Old Man Hammer's seeds sprouting in the garden.	7. ______________________
Summer came, and in the back of the garden grew a tall patch of sunflowers.	8. ______________________

At Home: Have students write a paragraph explaining the possible effect that the garden had on Old Man Hammer's life.

Draw Conclusions

To draw a **conclusion** about a character or an event in a story, you use facts from the story. You also use your own knowledge and experience. Drawing conclusions as you read can help you better understand a story.

Answer each question below. Base your conclusion on your own experience and on information from "City Green."

1. What kind of person is Marcy?

____

____

2. What details from the selection helped you to draw that conclusion?

____

____

3. What kind of relationship did Old Man Hammer and his neighbors have?

____

4. What details from the selection helped you to draw your conclusion?

____

____

____

5. Why did Old Man Hammer secretly plant seeds?

____

____

6. What details from the selection helped you draw that conclusion?

____

At Home: Have students draw a conclusion about the effect the community garden had on the neighborhood.

Name____________________ Date__________ **Practice 44**

Context Clues

When you read an unfamiliar word you can use **context clues**, or the words or sentences before or after the word, to help you determine the word's meaning.

Read the sentence or sentences. Use context clues to figure out the meaning of the underlined words. Write the meaning of each word.

1. The mother whale takes good care of its calf after it is born.

   calf means ______________________________

2. People joined together to rescue the whale when it was in trouble.

   rescue means ______________________________

3. The whales migrate from the north each winter and swim to the warm waters in the south. They return to the north again each summer.

   migrate means ______________________________

4. Many save-the-whale groups are working to protect these big creatures of the sea.

   creatures means ______________________________

5. Blue whales are mammoth and can grow to one hundred feet.

   mammoth means ______________________________

At Home: Have students point out the context clues in each sentence that helped them to determine the meaning of each word.

Name ____________________ Date ____________ **Practice 45**

Compare and Contrast

Read each object name. Answer the questions about each object to complete the chart. Write **Y** for **yes**. Write **N** for **no**.

A.

Is it	white?	round?	food?	fun?	hard?
baseball	____	____	____	____	____
onion	____	____	____	____	____
snowball	____	____	____	____	____
soap bubble	____	____	____	____	____

B. Use the completed chart to think about how the objects are alike and how they are different.

1. In what ways is the soap bubble different from the other objects?

____

2. How are snowballs and onions different?

____

3. How are baseballs and snowballs alike?

____

4. In what way are all 5 objects alike?

____

At Home: Have students add one more question to the chart. How do the objects compare using this new trait?

Name________________________ Date____________ **Practice 46**

Vocabulary

Write the letter of the word that best matches each definition.

1. When you have exchanged one thing for another, you have _____ it.	**a.** peaks
2. When the water in a stream has moved smoothly, it has _____.	**b.** handful
3. Hard, tiny pieces of things like rock or sand are known as _____.	**c.** traded
4. The amount you can hold in one hand is a _____.	**d.** canyons
5. The pointed tops of mountains are called _____.	**e.** grains
6. Deep valleys with steep sides are known as _____.	**f.** flowed

At Home: Have students write a paragraph using the vocabulary words.

A Mountain of Fun

Molly mixed paper, paste, and water. She wanted to use the material to make something. "I will make two mountains with tall *peaks*," she said. When the mountains were finished, Cliff placed sand in the *canyons* between the mountains. It took a large *handful* of sand to completely cover the canyon floor. "The *grains* will stick to the sticky surface and look like the dirt of a canyon," Cliff told Molly.

Next, Molly painted the mountain gray and Cliff painted the canyon brown. Then they *traded* places and added on another layer of paint.

Molly and Cliff stepped back to look at their finished model. There was just one thing missing. Molly knew what it was. Slowly she painted a strip of blue through the canyon. The water looked like it *flowed* .

1. What is another word for the top of a mountain?

____

2. Where did Cliff place sand?

____

3. How much sand did Cliff use?

____

4. What did the blue that Molly painted onto the model look like?

____

5. What did Molly do to help make the model?

____

At Home: Encourage students to name any famous mountains or canyons they know about. Where are they? Have they ever been to them?

Name____________________ Date____________ **Practice 47**

Story Comprehension

Answer the following questions about "The Sun, the Wind and the Rain."

1. Where does this story take place? ____________________

2. What two mountains are looked at in the story? ____________________

3. What kind of information does the story tell about the real mountain?

4. What happens when rivers rush down the earth mountain? ____________________

5. What makes Elizabeth cry? ____________________

6. Why don't either of the mountains stay the same? ____________________

At Home: Have students draw a picture of one of the scenes described in "The Sun, the Wind, and the Rain."

Name______________________________ Date______________ **Practice 48**

Use a Dictionary

Place each of the dictionary parts below in its proper place.

sizzle
adjective
sidewalk
to make music with your voice
SIDE
(sīz)

1. ______________ **—SIZZLE**

2. ______________ 1. a path by the side of a street (sīd′wôk) *noun*

3. silly 1. lacking common sense, foolish (sil′ē) ______________

4. sing 1. ____

(sing) *verb*

5. size 1. the amount of space an object takes up ______________ *noun*

6. ______________ 1. to make a hissing sound (siz′əl) *verb*

At Home: Ask students to look up the word silt and to put it in its proper place in the above dictionary page, writing in the definition, pronunciation, and part of speech.

Name________________________ Date____________ **Practice 49**

Compare and Contrast

Think about "The Sun, the Wind and the Rain." In what ways are the earth mountain and Elizabeth's mountain alike? How are they different? Complete the chart to compare the two mountains.

	earth mountain	**Elizabeth's mountain**
Formed when?	long ago	____________ ____________
Made of what?	rock and sandstone	____________ ____________
How big?	reaching up into the sky	____________ ____________
Rain does what?	____________ ____________	destroys it and carries it to sea

Why do you think the author wrote about the two kinds of mountains? Circle your answer.

- to show how big they are
- to show mountain canyons
- to show how mountains change over time

At Home: Have students share experiences they have had at the beach or the mountains. Encourage them to focus on the sights and sounds.

Name________________________________ Date______________ **Practice 50**

Draw Conclusions

A conclusion is what you decide after you have read a story. You can also use your own experience to help you **draw conclusions**.

Draw your conclusions about the story by answering each question.

Annie took a lot of pictures. There was one rock that looked like a bridge and another that looked like a wise old owl.

Annie wondered out loud if people had ever lived in this wonderful place.

"I'll show you something and you can decide for yourself," her father said.

It was already getting dark when they parked the car next to an enormous rock. Annie was astonished to see drawings of the horses and people.

"Native Americans made these pictures hundreds of years ago. Aren't they beautiful?" Annie's father said.

"Can we come back tomorrow when it's light enough for me to take a picture?"

1. Do you think Annie enjoyed her trip? ____________________

2. What information from the story helped you to draw your conclusion?

____

____

3. Where might Annie and her father be? ____________________

____

____

4. Had people ever lived in the place Annie visited? Explain. __________

____

At Home: Have students draw conclusions about whether or not Annie's father had ever visited this place before.

Name______________________ Date____________ Practice 51

Antonyms and Synonyms

Antonyms are words that have the opposite, or nearly opposite, meaning.

Synonyms are words that have the same, or nearly the same, meaning.

Antonyms	**Synonyms**
hot, cold	large, big

Choose a word from the list on the right that is a synonym or antonym for the word on the left. Write the word on the first line. On the second line, write **S** if the word pairs are synonyms. Write **A** if the word pairs are antonyms.

1. shout	______________	_____	different
2. like	______________	_____	won
3. help	______________	_____	distrust
4. less	______________	_____	dislike
5. noisy	______________	_____	yell
6. unusual	______________	_____	quiet
7. believe	______________	_____	down
8. lost	______________	_____	aid
9. angry	______________	_____	more
10. up	______________	_____	mad

At Home: Have students name a synonym and an antonym for **chilly.**

Name________________________ Date____________ **Practice 52**

Cause and Effect

A **cause** is what makes something happen. The **effect** is what happens as a result of the cause. You can use cause and effect to help you make predictions about what might happen next.

Read each paragraph. Write the cause that made the effect happen. Then write a sentence to make a prediction.

Jack grew apples to sell at the market. This year the apples were perfect. They had not been eaten by worms. Jack had found a new way to keep the worms away.

1. **Cause:** ____

____

2. **Effect:** The apples were perfect and hadn't been filled with worms.

3. **Predict** what Jack will do next year: ____________________

____

Anna decided to eat her lunch outside. She sat on a bench and took out her sandwich. Suddenly she heard a buzzing sound. There was a bee flying around Anna. The bee wanted a bite of her sandwich.

4. **Cause:** ____

____

5. **Effect:** A bee is buzzing around Anna.

6. **Predict** what Anna will do for lunch tomorrow: ____________

____

At Home: Have students predict what they would do if they were ten feet tall.

Name________________________ Date______________ **Practice 53**

Vocabulary

Identify and write down clues to the meaning of the underlined word in each question.

1. The <u>buffalo</u>, a large, furry animal with a hump on its back, is in danger of becoming extinct. ______________________________

2. The <u>darkness</u> of night was all around us, and there was no light to be seen. ______________________________

3. Did the way the <u>echoes</u> of my voice bounced off the mountain make me seem far away? ______________________________

4. As groups of animals traveled together across the plains, the noise the <u>herd</u> made was like thunder. ______________________________

____

5. The berries were <u>ripe</u> and juicy now that they were ready to eat.

____

6. To protect themselves from the sun, the two girls decided to <u>shelter</u> under a beach umbrella. ______________________________

____

At Home: Have students make up a crossword puzzle using the vocabulary words. Have them write a clue for each word.

A Return to Home

Long ago, a young *buffalo* walked across the Great Plains. As *darkness* came, she began to look for *shelter*. The buffalo called out for someone to help her find a place to sleep. But all she could hear were the *echoes* of her own voice.

The buffalo grew hungry. She ate some sweet, *ripe* berries. She also ate some small plants.

Suddenly, she saw another buffalo. She followed the other buffalo. The buffalo led her to a place where several *herds* rested together.

When some of the herd saw the newcomer, they gave her food. They also made a space where she could sleep.

1. What did the *buffalo* begin to look for?

____

2. What did the *buffalo* hear when she called out?

____

3. Why were the berries the *buffalo* ate sweet?

____

4. In what kind of groups do *buffalo* live?

____

5. Why did the young *buffalo* follow the other *buffalo*?

____

At Home: Invite students to talk about a story they like that has animals as characters.

Name______________________________ Date____________ **Practice 54**

Story Comprehension

Think about the story of Tiblo and Tanksi in "Dream Wolf." Then answer each question below.

QUESTIONS	ANSWERS
SETTINGS Where does the story take place?	1. ____________ 2. ____________ 3. ____________
CHARACTERS Who are the main characters?	4. ____________ 5. ____________ 6. ____________
PLOT What problem do Tiblo and Tanksi face?	7. ____________ ____________ ____________
EVENTS Where do Tiblo and Tanksi spend the night? What happens there? What happens when Tiblo wakes up and sees the wolf?	8. ____________ ____________ ____________ ____________ 9. ____________ ____________
CONCLUSION How does the story end?	10. ____________ ____________ ____________

At Home: Have students illustrate a scene from "Dream Wolf."

10

Name________________________________ Date______________ **Practice 55**

Use an Encyclopedia

Natural Bridge—Navigation

Natural Bridge is a bridge made from stone by nature. Wind or rain or rivers carved away the stone over many years. Usually softer stone is removed from under harder stone. A bridge of harder stone is all that remains.

Nauru is a small island country in the Pacific Ocean. It is the third smallest nation in the world. Monaco and Vatican City are smaller. It's greatest resource is phosphate, a substance used to make fertilizer.

Navajo, a Native American group who have lived in the southwestern United States since around 1000 A.D. They are the largest Native American group in the United States. Many members still live in houses called hogans, made of earth and logs. See also Indian, American

Naval Reserve. See Navy, United States

Fill in the blank spaces below based on the encyclopedia page.

Entry Words:

____

____

____

____

Cross-References:

____

____

Guide Words:

____

____

At Home: Ask students if they would look on this page for information about narwhal whales. Why or why not?

Name______________________________ Date______________ **Practice 56**

Cause and Effect

In "Dream Wolf," things happen that cause other events to occur. Answer the following questions about **cause** and **effect**.

1. Why do the people move from the plains to the hills and valleys?

   ____

2. What did Tiblo do when he became tired of picking berries? ______________________________

3. What effect did the sun going down have on the two children?

   ____

4. While the children slept, a wolf came into the cave and kept them warm. What effect did this have on Tiblo's dreams? ______________

   ____

5. The wolf led the children back to their camp. What did the children then ask the wolf? ______________________________

6. What did the people in the camp do when they saw the children coming down the hill? ______________________________

   ____

7. What has caused wolves to disappear from the hills where they used to live? ______________________________

8. When do the people say the wolves will return? ______________

   ____

Compare and Contrast

When you **compare** and **contrast** two things, you point out how they are the same and how they are different.

Look at the picture. Then answer the questions.

1. Name two ways that Sam and Frankie look alike. ____________

____

____

2. Name two ways that Sam and Frankie look different.

____

____

____

3. What is the same about what the two dogs are doing? ____________

____

4. What is different about what the two dogs are doing? ____________

____

At Home: Have students organize their observations of Sam and Frankie into a two-column chart. Label the columns "Alike" and "Different."

Context Clues

Context clues are words or sentences that can help you find the meaning of an unfamiliar word. You may find context clues in the text before or after the unfamiliar word.

Read the selection. Write a definition for each word or term.

There are more kinds of plants and animals living in the warm, wet rain forests than anywhere else on Earth. It is interesting to know how a rain forest works and why it is always so moist. The leaves of the trees catch rain. The rain then travels down the stems to the ground. The ground absorbs most of the water and the rest goes into rivers and streams. Under the ground, the roots of the trees absorb the water in the soil. Then the roots send the water up the trunk of each tree, out into its branches, and into its leaves. If you stand on the ground in a rain forest and look up, all you can see is leaves. The trees' leaves collect so much water that clouds form above them. The clouds fall again as rain. When it rains, the pattern begins all over again, with the leaves catching the rain.

1. **rain forest** ______________________________

____

2. **moist** ______________________________
3. **absorbs** ______________________________
4. **soil** ______________________________
5. **pattern** ______________________________

____

At Home: Ask students to use some of the new words in sentences.

Name________________________ Date____________ **Practice 59**

Important and Unimportant Information

When you read nonfiction, you need to be able to tell the difference between passages that include **important information**, or facts, about the main idea and passages that give **unimportant information**. Unimportant information does not add details about the main idea, although it may include interesting observations.

Read the following story. Draw a line under each sentence that contains important information about sea horses.

Sea Horses

"What kind of horse has no hair?" A sea horse, of course.

Sea horses live in warm water that is not very deep. They eat tiny things in the water that people cannot even see, as well as small fish. Not many fish like to eat sea horses though. They have too many bones.

Sea horses are clever artists. They turn into the colors of the plants around them so that they can hide from fish that hunt them. It would be wonderful to see a sea horse change from brown to yellow!

Copy a sentence that includes **unimportant** information. Then explain why the sentence does not add important information about sea horses.

____

____

____

____

At Home: Have students explain how they determined which information was important to learning about sea horses.

Name_______________________ Date_____________ **Practice 60**

Vocabulary

Supply the correct word from the list to complete each sentence.

ruin liquid capture serious skills struggles

1. A spider builds a web because it wants to catch, or ____________________, insects.
2. If you roll around on the grass in your best clothes, you might ____________________ them.
3. A ____________________ problem needs to be thought about deeply and carefully.
4. When a fly ____________________ to escape from a spider's web, it makes a great effort to try and get free.
5. Water is a ____________________, but ice is not.
6. Playing the piano and drawing are two ____________________ that I have mastered.

At Home: Have students write a short story using three or more of the vocabulary words.

Brave Little Spider

Little May was very *serious* about becoming a web spinner. There was one problem, though. She just didn't have the *skills*. Every time May tried to build a web, she would *ruin* it one way or another. "My poor little girl *struggles* so much," said her mother.

One day, a little boy tried to *capture* May's mother by putting her into a jar. May didn't know what to do. Then she had an idea! Quickly she began to spin a web over a small puddle of *liquid*.

As the boy walked through the web he lost his balance and fell. May and her mother were able to escape. May's mother was proud of her daughter. "Your webs might not be strong enough to catch bugs," May's mother said. "But they sure are strong enough to save me!"

1. How did May feel about wanting to be a web spinner?

____

2. What does May need to have to become a web spinner?

____

3. What does the little boy try to do?

____

4. Where did May spin her web to help her mother?

____

5. How did May's mother feel about May at the end of the story?

____

At Home: Have students use the italicized words from the story in sentences.

Name________________________________ Date______________ **Practice 61**

Story Comprehension

Use the story "Spiders at Work" to help you answer these questions.

1. How many legs does a spider have? ______________________

2. What is a bridge line? ______________________

____

3. How can you tell if a spider is a black widow? ______________________

____

____

4. Why do people need to look out for black widow spiders? ______________________

____

____

5. What kind of spiders do some people keep as pets? ______________________

6. How did the daddy-longlegs get its name? ______________________

____

7. Name some places that spiders can be found. ______________________

____

____

8. According to a Navaho folk tale, what did Spider Woman teach the Navaho people to do? ______________________

____

____

At Home: Ask students to imagine what it would be like to be a spider. Have them write a short story about a day as a spider.

Name__________________________ Date___________ **Practice 62**

Use a Dictionary

The word-history section of a dictionary entry tells how the word entered our language. *ME* stands for Middle English, an older form of English. *OE* stands for Old English, an even older form of English. *Fr* stands for French, and *OFr* stands for old French. Latin is also an old language.

leg the part of the body that is used for standing or walking *noun* (leg) ME *leggr*.

capture to grab or hold *verb* (kap′ chər) OFr< Latin *captura*

insect a small animal without a backbone *noun* (in sekt′) Latin *insectum*

spin to turn around and around *verb* (spin) ME *spinnen*

weave to spin a web or cocoon *verb* (wēv) OE *wefan*

Fill in the blanks in the chart below.

WORD	PRONUNCIATION	DEFINITION	PART OF SPEECH	ORIGIN
leg	(leg)	____________ ____________ ____________	noun	ME *leggr*
spin	(spin)	to turn around and around	_______	ME *spinnen*
_______	(wēv)	to spin a web or cocoon	verb	OE *wefan*
insect	(in′sekt)	a type of small animal without a backbone	_______	_______ _______
capture	_________	to grab or hold	verb	OFr< Latin *captura*

At Home: Ask students to look in an dictionary and find another word that comes from Middle English, Old English, French, Old French, or Latin.

Name____________________ Date__________ **Practice 63**

Important and Unimportant Information

People often read stories like "Spiders at Work" in order to answer questions that they have. Keeping such purposes in mind can help you sort out **important information** from **unimportant information**.

Decide whether or not each statement below is important to the given purpose. Write an **X** next to the information that is important.

Purpose: To find out which spiders can hurt people

____ **1.** The web looks pretty, but it is a trap for flies and other bugs.

____ **2.** Black widow spiders do not bite people very often.

____ **3.** The tarantula's bite is about as strong as a bee sting.

____ **4.** Spiders belong to a family of their own.

Purpose: To find out how a spider builds its web

____ **5.** The air helps the spider by blowing the bridge line from one plant to another.

____ **6.** Daddy-longlegs eat flies and mosquitoes.

____ **7.** The spider keeps building by going back and forth, and up and down.

____ **8.** The spider spins a sticky thread in a circle.

Purpose: To find out where spiders live

____ **9.** Some spiders are as small as the head of a pin.

____ **10.** Water spiders have their homes under water.

____ **11.** Ants have six legs, and spiders have eight legs.

____ **12.** One spider in South America lives in trees and eats small birds.

At Home: Ask students to illustrate one of the sentences on the page.

Name________________ Date________ **Practice 64**

Draw Conclusions

You can **draw conclusions** based on information from a story or from your own life. You can often draw conclusions from just a few clues.

Draw a conclusion from each passage below.

1. Sometimes, Jeff and Bill would fight over their toys. When this happened, their grandmother played games with them so they would forget why they were fighting.

   Conclusion: What can you tell about the boys' grandmother?

   ____

2. The flowers had just started to peek out from beneath the ground. The park was full of people wearing jackets and hats that they didn't need.

   Conclusion: What time of year is it? How do you know? __________

   ____

3. Kim decided to try out for the baseball team. Her brother said she was better than he had been at her age.

   Conclusion: Is Kim's brother older or younger? ________________

4. "It is too bad that so many people are afraid of spiders. Most spiders don't bite! Many are even helpful. They eat bugs that might bite you," said Jack.

   Conclusion: How does Jack feel about spiders? ________________

5. May spilled her milk. Her teacher still had something kind to say about May. May's teacher was good when things went wrong.

   Conclusion: What is May's teacher like? ______________________

At Home: Have students draw another conclusion about each of the passages.

Antonyms and Synonyms

Antonyms are words with opposite meanings.
Synonyms are words with the same or similar meanings.

Replace the underlined word with a synonym. Write the answer on the line.

1. The class was excited about going on the trip. ____________________
2. They asked their relatives for help. ____________________
3. It is silent in the park at night. ____________________
4. They were curious to learn about the animals. ____________________

Write an antonym for each underlined word.

5. The campers were unprepared when the storm appeared.

____

6. They did not want to spend all night in their tents.

____

7. After a brief shower, the ground was soaked.

____

8. Everyone wondered if the rain would continue.

____

At Home: Ask students to form antonyms for **usual, happy,** and **pleased** by adding the prefix **un-** or **dis-** to each word.

Name________________________ Date____________ **Practice 66**

Compare and Contrast

Read the list of animals. Use what you know to fill in the chart.

hamsters	dogs	goats	frogs	geese	parrots	rabbits
goldfish	cats	ducks	sheep	horses	lizards	canaries

Favorite Animals

May Live on Farms	May Live in Homes	Can Swim	Can Fly

Choose two animals from the chart. Write how they are alike and how they are different.

____

____

____

____

____

____

At Home: Have students compare and contrast two of the animals on the chart. Have them look at such topics as size, weight, and temperament.

Vocabulary

Supply the correct words from the list to complete each sentence. The same vocabulary word is used twice in each example.

crops earthquake hatch respect soldiers woven

1. ________________ are plants we grow for food. Wheat and corn are two kinds of ________________ farmers grow in the United States.
2. When the ground started to shake, I knew we were having an ________________. Luckily, no one was hurt during the ________________, but some buildings were damaged.
3. The hen sits on her eggs to keep them warm until they ________________. Watch the eggs ________________ to see the little chicks!
4. I really admire and ________________ Mrs. Jackson. As one of the best teachers at school, she has earned everyone's ________________.
5. My cousins joined the army because they wanted to be ________________. Besides fighting in wars, ________________ also help to protect and rebuild cities and countries.
6. Some of the most beautiful blankets in the world are ________________ by Native Americans. Yarn is carefully ________________ together in different colored strips to make lovely patterns.

At Home: Have students use each vocabulary word in another sentence.

Two Birds in the Hand

Two *soldiers* were marching through a field. The men were returning to their families. They had been helping people recover from an *earthquake*.

Suddenly the soldiers heard a sound. On the edge of a row of *crops* they found a bird's nest. One little bird was about to *hatch*. Another was already out. There was no mother bird. For several minutes the men waited for the mother bird. Finally, they realized that the baby birds were alone.

"Poor little birds," said one soldier. He placed the nest inside his big *woven* coat. "I will take them home."

"You are a great man," said the other soldier. "You *respect* all life, no matter how big or small!"

1. Where did the soldiers find the bird's nest?

____

2. What in the story was *woven*?

____

3. What was one little bird about to do?

____

4. What had the soldiers been doing at the beginning of the story?

____

5. Why did the soldier feel sorry for the birds?

____

At Home: Help students think about and discuss why baby animals might need help to survive.

Name________________ Date________ **Practice 68**

Story Comprehension

Answer the following questions about "Web Wonders."

1. Stories may be written to give information, to entertain, or both. Why do you think this story was written? ________________

2. In the story, why did enemy arrows bounce off Genghis Khan's soldiers? ________________

3. Do you think this story is true? Why or why not? ________________

4. How can baby spiders travel so far? ________________

5. Why can't farmers raise spiders for their silk? ________________

6. If scientists could make something as strong as spider's silk, what would they use it for?

____

At Home: Ask students to explain why scientists are interested in making humanmade spider silk. Have students suggest some other possible uses for it.

Name________________________ Date______________ **Practice 69**

Use a Resource

Study the sample dictionary entry. Then take a careful look at the encyclopedia entry that is below it.

nylon a strong fabric manufactured from chemicals. Nylon is used to make thread, clothes, stockings, tires for automobiles, tents for camping, and many other things. **ny-lon** (nī′lon) *noun.*

nylon is the family name for a group of materials made from chemicals. Coal, water, and chemicals are blended to make a wide variety of products. Nylon can be both strong and flexible. In 1937, it was first used to replace silk in stockings. Wallace Carothers developed special ways to make nylon for the Dupont Company. The first nylon he produced melted at low temperatures. If you made a dress out of this early nylon, a hot iron would melt it. By adding other chemicals, the nylon we know today was created. Qiana is a type of nylon that is commonly used in modern clothes. It has many of the qualities of silk.

Now read the selections below. Decide if they might have come from a dictionary entry or an encyclopedia entry. Write *dictionary* or *encyclopedia* to answer the questions below.

1. Which resource tells the history of *nylon*?

   ____

2. Which resource defines *nylon* as a strong fabric manufactured from chemicals? ______________________________

3. Which resource tells you how to pronounce *nylon*?

   ____

4. Which resource tells you about a type of *nylon* called Qiana?

   ____

5. Which resource tells you that *nylon* is a noun?

   ____

At Home: Ask students where they might look to find predictions about how nylon will be used in the future.

Name________________________________ Date____________ **Practice 70**

Important and Unimportant Information

When you have specific questions or purposes for reading, you should look for **important information** to answer your questions. **Unimportant information** will not suit your specific purpose.

Read the story. Then write the letters of the sentences that are important to each purpose. Each sentence may be used more than once.

(a) Scientists hope to make a cloth one day that will be as strong as spider silk. **(b)**They may have gotten the idea from an old story. **(c)** The story says that arrows bounced off some soldiers because spider silk was woven into their clothes.

(d) Spiders make spider silk from their bodies. **(e)** Baby spiders hatch from eggs and then spin a line of silk and wait for the wind to carry them to a new home. **(f)** Tarantulas, who live in holes in the ground, do not make silk.

(g) People have respect for spiders because of the spiders' skills at building. **(h)** Farmers like them because they eat bugs.

(i) Spiders spin webs to catch the bugs that they eat. **(j)** Scientists think a giant silk web could capture a plane. **(k)** It could also be used to help hold a bridge in place during an earthquake.

1. **Purpose:** To find out why scientists are interested in spider silk

   ____

2. **Purpose:** To find out facts about spiders ____________________
3. **Purpose:** To find out other uses for spiders besides for their silk _____
4. **Purpose:** To find out how spiders have helped people __________
5. **Purpose:** To find a story about the use of spider silk __________

At Home: Ask students to underline the important facts in the story.

Name________________________________ Date______________ **Practice 71**

Antonyms and Synonyms

A **synonym** is a word that has the same, or almost the same, meaning as another word. An **antonym** is a word that has the opposite, or almost opposite, meaning of another word.

Synonyms: *beautiful, pretty* **Antonyms**: *quiet, noisy*

Choose the word from the box that is a synonym for the underlined word in each sentence. Write the word.

turned	covered	gripe	heap	wave

1. May watched the trees <u>sway</u> in the wind. ______________
2. All the garden tools were in a <u>pile</u> in the corner. ______________
3. Suddenly the rain <u>changed</u> into hail. ______________
4. Clouds <u>hid</u> the mountain's peaks. ______________
5. It didn't do any good to <u>complain</u> about the cold. ______________

In each group of four words, circle the two words that are either synonyms or antonyms. Write **synonym** if the words are synonyms and **antonym** if the words are antonyms.

6. rough smooth take hide ______________
7. sing walk stride branch ______________
8. look chase eat stare ______________
9. pull rush push sift ______________
10. gray clean dirty proud ______________

At Home: Have students tell if the following word pairs are synonyms or antonyms: **throw/catch; small/little; soft/hard; rest/nap.**

Context Clues

The words and sentences around a word can help you discover its meaning. **Context clues** can be synonyms, antonyms, or examples. Some sentences even provide an exact definition for a word.

Write a definition for each boldfaced word.

1. It was an **error.** Luckily, we could fix the incorrect word.

____

2. They will **admit** everyone to the play. They will let in children first.

____

3. Many planets move in wide circles. For example, the earth **revolves** around the sun.

____

4. Erin wants to **adopt** a dog and take care of it at her home.

____

5. The afternoon seemed **endless.** The children thought it would go on forever.

____

6. The soldier played the **bugle,** a small instrument like a trumpet, every morning and evening.

____

At Home: Ask students to think of some context clues that could be used for the word **shelter.**

Name________________________ Date____________ **Practice 73**

Unit 2 Vocabulary Review

A. Supply the correct word from the box.

capture	soldiers	darkness	peaks	shelter	halfway

The ____________ climbed up the mountain. There were many high ____________. They needed to ____________ the tower on top of the highest peak. About ____________ up, they heard a loud bang. They ran for ____________ behind a rock. They waited for night to fall. Then they climbed the rest of the way in ____________. They took the army in the tower by surprise.

B. Label each statement **true** or **false**. If false, explain why.

1. You can pour a liquid. ____________

____

2. Birds hatch eggs. ____________

____

3. You'll get sick if you eat a ripe tomato. ____________

____

4. Echoes don't make any noise. ____________

____

At Home: Have students draw a picture to illustrate a vocabulary word. They can then write a sentence telling what the picture shows.

Name ______________________ Date ____________ **Practice 74**

Unit 2 Vocabulary Review

A. Choose the correct word to write on each line. You need two words for each item.

grains	handful	buffalo	herds	earthquake	area

1. Damon took a ______________ of sand. Then he let the ______________ fall through his fingers.
2. ______________ travel together in ______________.
3. An ______________ is rare in this ______________ of the country.

B. Supply the correct word from the box.

serious	respect	struggles	schedule

1. Everybody should ______________ the judge.
2. Tanya made a ______________ mistake.
3. Martha ______________ to stay awake until the end of the show.
4. We need to keep on ______________, or we won't finish at noon.

At Home: Have students write a journal entry about something that is important to them. They should use a vocabulary word in each sentence.

10

Name_______________________ Date_____________ **Practice 75**

Main Idea

The **main idea** is the major point that an author wants readers to understand. **Supporting details** are small examples and reasons that explain the main idea.

For each main idea below, write some possible supporting details.

Main Idea: Matt helps out around the house.

Supporting Details:

1. ______________________________

____

2. ______________________________

____

3. ______________________________

____

Main Idea: Ashley is a great baseball player.

Supporting Details:

4. ______________________________

____

5. ______________________________

____

6. ______________________________

____

At Home: Have students add one more supporting detail to each of the main ideas above.

Vocabulary

Supply the correct answers.

1. If you wanted to hear music at your party, why would you invite a **musician**? ______________________________

2. What would you hear at a **concert**? ______________________________

3. After learning how to play the drums, a person might join an **orchestra**. What is that? ______________________________

4. What are some musical **instruments**? ______________________________

5. How does a **conductor** help members of a band to play music? ______________________________

6. Why would you stay home from school if you felt **ill**? ______________________________

At Home: Have students write a story using all the vocabulary words.

A Special Touch

The *concert* was about to begin. But where was the *conductor*? Oh no! He was *ill*! How would the *orchestra* know what to do?

Each *musician* had a different idea. The violin player thought the orchestra should play without the conductor. The piano player thought she should be the conductor. The horn player thought the musicians should give a speech about each *instrument* they played. The drum player thought they should all go out to lunch.

Then the conductor's wife came in. "I have watched my husband practice. I can do his job," she said.

That night the orchestra gave one of its greatest concerts! Even the local newspapers agreed.

1. What is a person who plays music called?

____

2. What are a violin, a piano, and a horn each called?

____

3. What is another name for a group of *musicians* playing together?

____

4. Who was too ill to be in the concert?

____

5. How was the orchestra's problem solved?

____

At Home: Ask students how they would have solved the problem faced by the orchestra.

Name ______________________ Date ____________ **Practice 77**

Story Comprehension

Match each character from “Moses Goes to a Concert” with each statement in the right column. Write the letter on the line.

1. Moses _____	**a.** feels vibrations with her feet.
2. Mr. Samuels _____	**b.** plays on the marimba.
3. Ann _____	**c.** has a new set of drums.
4. The percussionist _____	**d.** takes his students to a concert.

Answer the following questions about “Moses Goes to a Concert.”

5. Who do the children meet at the concert?

____

____

6. Why did Mr. Samuels give the children balloons before the concert?

____

____

7. What is a percussionist?

____

____

8. What does Moses tell his parents at the end of the story?

____

____

At Home: Have students write a sentence about how Moses feels at the end of the story.

8

Name________________________ Date____________ **Practice 78**

Use a Diagram

Some of the hand positions for letters in American Sign Language look like the written letters. Others use movements that appear to be drawing the letter in the air.

Study these letters. Explain how the fingers are positioned to look like the letter they represent. The first one is done for you.

1. C **The thumb and other four fingers form a C shape.**

2. 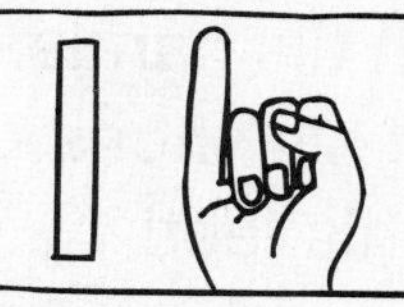

____

3. 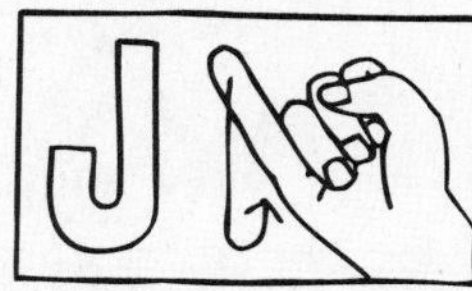

____

4. 

____

5. 

____

6. 

____

7. 

____

8. 

____

____

At Home: Have students demonstrate the American Sign Language letters shown on this page.

Name______________________________ Date____________ **Practice 79**

Main Idea

To understand a passage better, separate the main idea from the details that support it. The **main idea** is the most important point. **Supporting details** are smaller points that explain the main idea.

Read the following sentences about "Moses Goes to a Concert." Write the main idea of the passage and then write the supporting details.

Moses has a new set of drums. He likes to play with his new drums, but he can't hear the sound they make. Moses is deaf. He can, however, feel the vibration of his drums with his hands. To feel even more of the vibrations, Moses takes off his shoes. Now he can feel his new drums with his hands and his feet!

Main Idea:

1. ____

____

Supporting Details:

2. ____

____

3. ____

____

4. ______________________

____

____

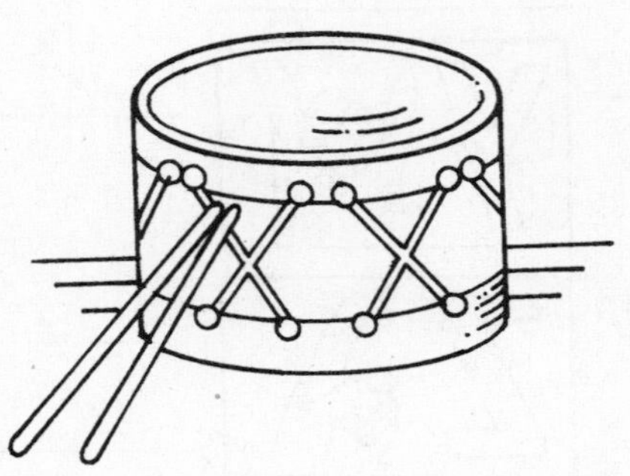

At Home: Have students read a paragraph from an article in a childrens' magazine or newspaper. Then ask them to write down the main idea and supporting details of the paragraph.

Name______________________ Date___________ **Practice 80**

Summarize

When you **summarize**, you tell only the most important things that happened. Read each passage below. Then write a summary.

1. Last summer, Crystal and her parents drove to Florida. On the way, their car broke down. They worried that they might not make it to Florida. However, they got their car fixed and drove there the next morning.

   Summary: ____

   ____

2. In Florida, they visited Crystal's grandma. Grandma loved to garden. She grew lemon trees, orange trees, and many different types of flowers. She gardened every day.

   Summary: ____

   ____

3. Crystal asked Grandma, "Can I work in the garden, too?" Grandma said yes. First, Crystal chose the kind of flowers she wanted. Crystal chose roses. Then, she planted seeds and watered them every day. Grandma said that Crystal's roses would bloom in the spring.

   Summary: ____

   ____

4. After two weeks in Florida, it was time to go home. Crystal and her parents hugged Grandma. Crystal felt sad about leaving, but she knew that they would come back in the spring.

   Summary: ____

   ____

At Home: Have students write a one-paragraph summary of the story on this page.

Name________________________ Date____________ **Practice 81**

Context Clues

When you find an unfamiliar word, read the words and sentences around it. They often can help you figure out the word's meaning.

Look at the underlined word in each example. Circle the words and phrases that help you tell what the word means. Then mark an **X** next to the meaning that fits the underlined word.

1. The musicians walked onto the stage. People clapped and waved.

The concert was about to begin.

_____ drums _____ musical performance _____ game

2. The singer sang a very high note. She broke a window.

_____ red _____ apple pie _____ sound in music

3. She is a percussionist. She plays the piano, the drums, and many other instruments.

_____ type of musician _____ large van _____ baby duck

4. Mozart is a famous composer. He wrote many beautiful songs.

_____ cab driver _____ dog food _____ person who creates a musical work

5. He played a pretty melody on the piano. I asked, "What is the name of that song?"

_____ green _____ tune _____ bat

At Home: Have students look up each underlined word in a dictionary to check the meaning.

Story Elements

Understanding the **characters** and the **setting** of a story can help you determine the **plot** of the story.

Read the passage below. Then answer the questions.

Ricardo's art teacher said, "For homework tonight, I would like each of you to paint someone who is special to you." Ricardo decided to paint his cat, Speedy.

That night, Ricardo took out some paint and paper. "Okay, Speedy," he said. "I'm going to paint you. Stand still!" Speedy ran over to Ricardo, jumped on his lap, jumped off his lap, ran into the kitchen, ran into Ricardo's room, pushed a pillow off the bed, and disappeared into the bathroom. "Speedy, stay still!" Ricardo shouted out. "I have to paint you!"

Suddenly the cat appeared again and began to run in circles around Ricardo. Ricardo sat down and thought about what to do next. Suddenly, Ricardo had an idea. "I know—I'll paint Speedy on the go!" he said.

When Ricardo brought his picture to school the next day, everyone liked it. "I'm lucky to have such a fast cat," he said.

1. Who are the main characters in this story? ____________________

2. Where does the story take place? ____________________

____

3. What is Ricardo's problem? ____________________

4. How does Ricardo solve this problem? ____________________

____

5. What is the plot of this story? ____________________

____

At Home: Have students write a few sentences explaining why they would or would not like to have Speedy as a pet.

Vocabulary

Supply the correct words from the list.

blossoms dawn faded imaginary miserable shallow

1. When a flower loses its color, it has ______________________.

2. A very unhappy person feels ______________________.

3. If a pond or lake is not deep, we describe it as ______________________.

4. ______________________ is the time of day when the sun first rises.

5. A story that you make up in your mind is ______________________.

6. In spring, many fruit trees produce lovely flowers called ______________.

At Home: Have students look up the vocabulary words in a dictionary and make vocabulary cards for each word to use as a study tool.

Carmen's Garden

One day a mouse named Carmen woke up at *dawn.* She liked to garden early in the morning.

Carmen's garden was behind her house near a stream that was *shallow.* Every day Carmen began by watering seeds she had planted. For weeks she watered and waited. But nothing happened! Waiting made Carmen *miserable.* After weeks of waiting, her hope for pretty flowers had *faded.*

Then one day, she spotted little green stems popping up. She couldn't believe it. "This must be *imaginary*!" she shouted. "The seeds are growing!"

Soon her garden was filled with the *blossoms* of hundreds of flowers.

1. What is the first moment of day called?

____

2. When a stream is not deep, what is it?

____

3. How does waiting make Carmen feel?

____

4. Why does the garden seem *imaginary* to Carmen?

____

5. Why did Carmen have to wait so long?

____

At Home: Ask students to identify the main idea of the story. Then ask them to point out the supporting details.

Name____________________________ Date____________ **Practice 84**

Story Comprehension

Think about the story of Fernando, the little painter. Then finish each sentence by writing the missing word on the blank line. Write that word on the crossword puzzle.

ACROSS

1. The smooth and white __________ houses reminded Fernando of paper.
4. Fernando lived in the village of __________ Grande.
6. Everyone said __________ words about Fernando's paintings.
8. The color yellow is made from dried __________ in the meadow.
9. Soon all the neighbors asked Fernando if he would paint their __________.
10. Above the door Fernando painted the words Casa Familia __________.

DOWN

2. The color __________ is made from the charcoal of a burned tree stump.
3. Fernando's teacher taught him how the country people of Panama made their __________.
5. The color blue is made from __________ that grow deep in the jungle.
7. The __________ brought out chairs and watched Fernando paint.

At Home: Have students think of two more clues and words to add to the puzzle.

Name________________________ Date____________ **Practice 85**

Use a Map

Maps often show more than roads, towns, and the borders of countries. Lines drawn on a map can show many different kinds of information. Sometimes an area on a map is colored or shaded to give information about that area.

Look at this map of a playground. Follow the instructions below to add more information to this map.

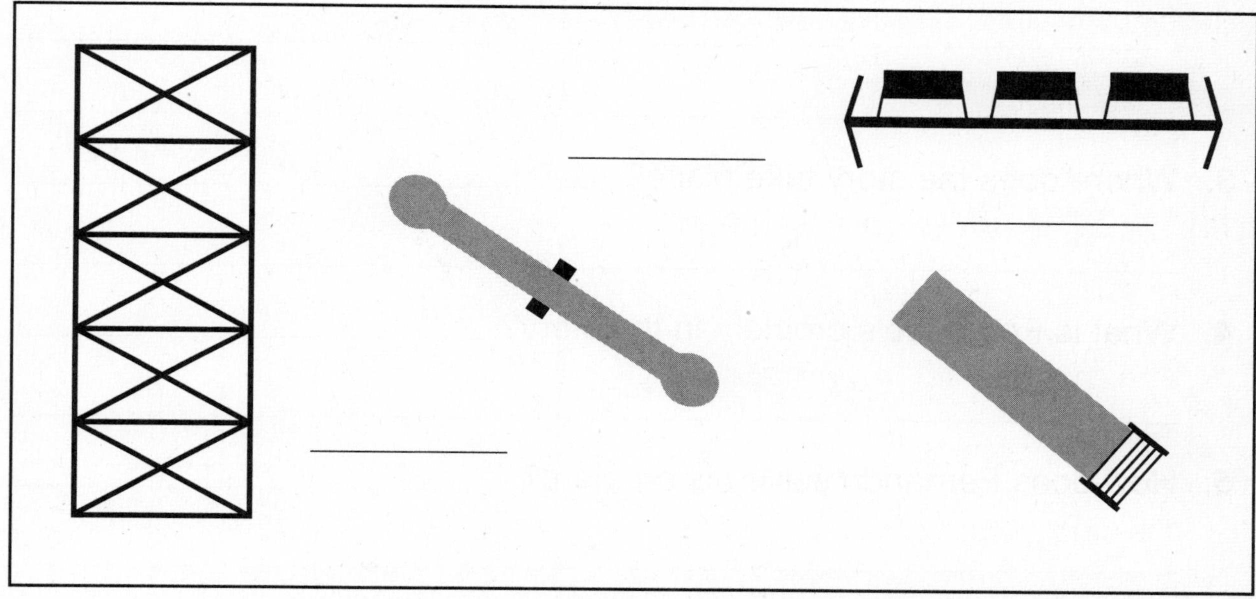

1. Draw a solid line around the swing sets and slides. This area has sand on the ground.
2. Write the word *sand* inside the area marked off by the solid line.
3. Draw a broken line around the gym bars. This area has rubber mats on the ground.
4. Write the word *rubber* next to this area.
5. Draw a double line around the seesaw. This area has grass on the ground.
6. Write the word *grass* next to this area.

At Home: Ask students to make a map of the playground at their school or in their neighborhood.

Story Elements

Choose a word from the list that describes Fernando, and write it on the line.

happy bored busy tired sad talented

1. Fernando is ________
2. Explain your word choice. ______________________________

____

____

3. Where does the story take place? ______________________________

____

4. What is Fernando's problem in the story? ______________________________

____

5. How does Fernando solve his problem? ______________________________

____

6. What do people from the village ask Fernando to do at the end of the story? ______________________________

At Home: Have students choose a different word from the list to describe Fernando, and explain their choice.

Name_______________________ Date___________ **Practice 87**

Summarize

Summarize each of the events in the story below. You may want to describe how Bonita feels as well as what she does.

1. **Event 1:** Bonita and her class were writing short stories about their families. Bonita felt excited. She brought in some old family pictures to help give her ideas about her story.

____

____

2. **Event 2:** Bonita wrote about her grandfather. Then, Bonita painted a picture of him to go along with her story. Bonita was happy with the way her story was turning out.

____

____

3. **Event 3:** Just then, a gust of wind blew through an open window. Bonita's story flew right out the window. "Now my story is ruined!" Bonita said sadly.

____

____

4. **Event 4:** Bonita looked at her family photos. Her grandfather was smiling. Suddenly, Bonita began to smile. "I bet I can write another story about my grandfather," she said. "This one will be even better than the last!"

____

____

____

At Home: Have students watch a TV show and write a one-paragraph summary of it.

Name________________________ Date____________ **Practice 88**

Context Clues

When you are reading, you often discover new words. When you come across a puzzling word, look at the words and phrases near it and think about what is happening in the story. These **context clues** often can help you figure out what the word means.

Read each passage.Then use context clues to decide what the underlined word means. Circle the letter next to the correct meaning.

1. She likes to paint landscapes: fields, forests, and ocean shores.

a. pictures of people

b. pictures of the land

2. Fernando painted blossoms on the wall of his house. The large purple flowers looked as if they were creeping up the wall.

a. fruits

b. flowers

3. I woke up at dawn. The sky was becoming lighter.

a. the first light that appears in the morning

b. a math teacher

4. Her art is improving. Each new painting is better than the one before.

a. getting better

b. feeling sick

5. My class went to see a Chinese art exhibit last week. We saw many beautiful paintings.

a. show

b. dance

At Home: Have students write a short story using some of the words above.

Name____________________________ Date____________ **Practice 89**

Make Inferences

Sometimes you must **infer**, or figure out, what is happening in a story from clues that the author gives. Read each of the following passages. Then answer each question.

It was Roxanne's birthday, and she was hoping that someone would give her a book about airplanes. Her Aunt Jackie brought her a present in a box. It was just the right size for a book. Roxanne tore open the package. "I can't wait to find out what is!" she said.

1. How do you think Roxanne felt as she opened up the package?

____

2. Which clues helped you make your inference? ____________________

____

Roxanne opened the box and took out a pair of socks. She looked down at them for a minute and sighed very quietly. "Oh . . ." Then she smiled. "Thanks, Aunt Jackie. Just what I needed." Roxanne hugged her aunt.

3. How does Roxanne feel about her present? ____________________

4. Which clues helped you make your inference? ____________________

____

5. How does Roxanne feel about her Aunt Jackie? ____________________

____

6. Which clues helped you make your inference? ____________________

____

____

At Home: Have students write a sentence or two describing what they think will happen next.

Name______________________ Date__________ **Practice 90**

Vocabulary

gazed costume pattern attic examined anxious

Answer the following questions.

1. If you were *anxious* about something, would you be worried or calm?

____

2. Would you be more likely to find a *pattern* on flowery wallpaper or in a pile of mud?

____

3. If you *gazed* at the sky, would you look at it for a long time or a short time?

____

4. When you are in an *attic* are you in the basement of a house or just under the roof?

____

____

5. Would you wear a *costume* while acting in a play or while taking a bath?

____

____

____

6. If you *examined* something, would you look at it carefully or just glance at it?

____

At Home: Have students use each of the vocabulary words in a sentence.

Guy's Holiday

Guy could not wait for Thanksgiving. He was *anxious* to show his Aunt Cora his Pilgrim *costume*.

When Aunt Cora arrived, she *gazed* at Guy. "My, Pilgrim, how you have grown!" she said.

After dinner, Aunt Cora and Mama told stories of their childhood. Mama went up to the *attic* and brought down a box filled with photos. Guy *examined* each photo.

In one, young Aunt Cora wore a dress with a *pattern* of leaves. It looked just like the dress she had on! "I guess some things never change!" Aunt Cora exclaimed.

After they finished looking at the photographs they ate dessert. This year they had four different kinds of pie.

1. What did Guy wear on Thanksgiving?

2. How did Guy feel about showing his costume to his aunt?

3. What did Guy's mother get from the *attic*?

4. What was on Aunt Cora's dress?

5. Why did Aunt Cora say that some things never change?

At Home: Have students list some of the things they do on Thanksgiving or on another special holiday.

Name______________________ Date__________ **Practice 91**

Story Comprehension

Look back over "The Patchwork Quilt." Then complete the chart below.

1. Setting of story	
2. Main characters	
3. Beginning of story	
4. Middle of story	
5. End of story	

Now match each patch of clothing or fabric with the person it belonged to in the story.

______	**6.** gold dress	**a.** Grandma
______	**7.** piece of old quilt	**b.** Mama
______	**8.** red shirt	**c.** Tanya
______	**9.** African princess costume	**d.** Jim
______	**10.** blue corduroy pants	**e.** Ted

At Home: Have students write a sentence explaining why the patchwork quilt was important to Tanya and her family.

Name______________________ Date____________ **Practice 92**

Use a Diagram

A **diagram** can help you see how to put something together. Use these diagrams and directions to create a square from a traditional quilt pattern.

This square is called an Indian Trail. It's also been called Forest Path or Winding Walk. As you can see, it looks like a path winding around and around.

Here are the two sizes of triangles that complete the diagram.

1. Start by drawing four sets of three small triangles. Draw them from each corner as shown at right. Then color them in. Use the dotted outlines as a guide.

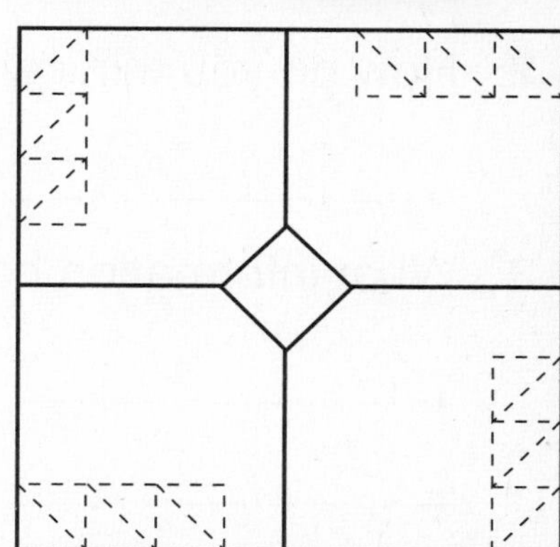

2. Add four big triangles to the square as shown. Then color in.

3. Add four sets of three small triangles to the inside of the square as shown.

4. Color in those triangles to complete the quilt.

At Home: Ask students to make their own simple design for a quilt.

Name________________________________ Date______________ **Practice 93**

Make Inferences

An **inference** is very much like a conclusion. A conclusion is almost certainly true. An inference is probably true.

Read each of the following passages about "The Patchwork Quilt." Then answer each question.

Grandma's eyes grew distant and dark. She turned away from Tanya and looked out the window for a long time, rubbing the material between her fingers.

1. What do you think Grandma was thinking about?

____

2. How do you think she felt as she looked out the window?

____

3. What information helped you make your inferences?

____

____

Finally, Grandma was ready to do the quilting, but she had one very important thing to add.

4. What "very important thing" did Grandma add to the quilt? ______________

____

5. When did you learn about the very important thing Grandma wanted to add?

____

6. Why do you think Grandma didn't tell Tanya what she was going to do?

____

At Home: Have students write a sentence or two explaining whether they think Tanya will teach her children about quiltmaking.

Main Idea

Read the following paragraphs. Then fill in the details that support the main ideas.

Yesterday, Carl went to the store. His mom and dad are fixing up his room. Carl bought green, brown, and orange paint for the walls and ceiling. Carl asked his mom to order a white shade for the window. For the floor, Carl hopes to find a red rug. Carl's mom thinks that his room will look like a rainbow.

Main Idea: Carl's mom and dad are fixing up his room.

Supporting details:

1. ______________________________
2. ______________________________
3. ______________________________

Gina went out to lunch with her friend, Wendy. Both girls had hamburgers. For dessert, Gina had a banana split. Wendy had fresh fruit. After lunch, the two friends went shopping.

Main Idea: Gina went out to lunch with her friend, Wendy.

Supporting details:

1. ______________________________
2. ______________________________
3. ______________________________

At Home: Have students read a short magazine or newspaper article and identify a main idea and two supporting details.

Multiple-Meaning Words

A word with **multiple meanings** has more than one meaning. The words and sentences around a word are called its **context.** Reading the words and sentences around a word can help you choose the correct meaning.

Read each sentence below. Circle the letter of the best meaning of each underlined word. Then, write a new sentence for the underlined word, using the meaning that you did **not** circle.

1. Tanya's quilt will last a long time.

a. at the end **b.** stay in good shape

____

2. She lost her hat.

a. no longer had **b.** failed to win

____

3. I like eating jam and bread.

a. a sweet food made with fruit **b.** put into a tight space

____

4. I stood in line at the store.

a. a long, thin mark **b.** people standing one after the other

____

At Home: Have students underline the context clue that helped them to define the underlined word in each sentence.

Name____________________________ Date______________ **Practice 96**

Story Elements

Understanding the main **characters** and the **setting** can help you understand what happens in a story.

Read the story below. Then answer the questions.

Today in class, everyone was supposed to write a story. Jamar couldn't think of anything to write about, so he asked his friends for some ideas.

Erica said, "Write about horses."

Pedro said, "Write about a ship."

Bill suggested, "Write about a doctor."

He raised his hand. "Mr. Diaz, what should I do?" he said. "I'll never think of a story. I asked all my friends, but I don't want to write about the things they suggested."

Mr. Diaz said, "Usually, it's a good idea to write about things you like."

Jamar thought about it. "I like baseball. I know! I'll write a story about a baseball player who becomes an all-star!"

1. Where does the story take place? ______________________________

____

2. Who is the main character? ______________________________

____

3. What is Jamar's problem? ______________________________

____

4. What does Jamar decide to do at the end of the story?

____

____

At Home: Have students write a few sentences explaining how Jamar tries to solve his problem.

Name______________________________ Date____________ **Practice 97**

Vocabulary

Write the vocabulary word that best fits in each of the sentences below.

combine invented located prairie stumbled wilderness

1. Let's ______________________ your hard work with my good ideas. By joining together, we can do a much better job.
2. The scientist was well-known for thinking of useful new things. He ______________________ egg timers and staplers, and he even made the first nonstick pan!
3. I live on Fire Street between the courthouse and the library. Where is your house ______________________?
4. I was camping in the forest. Crickets were singing, and frogs were croaking. It was so lovely being out there in the ______________________.
5. The flat, grassy fields seemed like they would never end, and I hadn't seen a tree for miles. "This has to be the biggest ______________________ in the United States," I thought to myself.
6. My brother stepped on his shoelace, ______________________, and then cried out as he fell down.

At Home: Have students think of other words that mean almost the same thing as the vocabulary words. Then have them use these words as clues for a vocabulary puzzle, crossword puzzle, or game.

Save the Animals!

Jed left his home on the *prairie*. He hoped to reach the edge of the *wilderness* before the sun set. He had something important to do.

Jed had *invented* a way to protect animals from floods. He wanted to show his invention to some of the animals along the way. The problem was, he couldn't find any animals! By late afternoon, Jed was about to give up. Suddenly he *stumbled* across a fox and her young. "Get away!" the fox shouted. "You will not hurt my babies and me!"

"I am here to help you," said Jed. "Let's *combine* what we know to save the animals. You tell me where the other animals are *located,* and I will share my invention with them."

The fox thought about it for a moment. Then she agreed. "I will show you," she said. "Follow me!"

1. Who *stumbled* across a fox?

____

2. Where was Jed's home?

____

3. What had Jed *invented*?

____

4. Where was Jed walking?

____

5. Why did Jed want to get to the animals?

____

At Home: Encourage students to think of ways that animals might be protected from hunters.

Story Comprehension

In "Pecos Bill," Cowboy Sam and Cowgirl Pam tell a story to Cookie and the ranch hands. "Pecos Bill" is a story within a story. Fill in the chart for each story.

	Main Story	Story Within a Story
Setting	______________________ ______________________	______________________ ______________________
Characters	______________________ ______________________ ______________________ ______________________	______________________ ______________________ ______________________ ______________________
Beginning	______________________ ______________________	______________________ ______________________
Middle	______________________ ______________________ ______________________ ______________________ ______________________ ______________________	______________________ ______________________ ______________________ ______________________ ______________________ ______________________
End	______________________ ______________________	______________________ ______________________

At Home: Ask students to circle the part of the chart that represents the plot.

Name____________________ Date__________ **Practice 99**

Use a Map

Use the map to answer the questions.

1. Some farmers asked Paul and Babe to clear land for farming. In one day, with a few swings of his huge ax, Paul removed every tree in two states. In which two states did he do this?

____

2. Paul Bunyan took a shovel and dug out Puget Sound on the West Coast. In which state did this take place? ______________

3. Babe needed new shoes. Paul needed a lot of iron to make four shoes Babe's size. Paul had to dig out three huge brand new iron mines. In which Midwestern state did he do this? ______________

4. When Babe was thirsty, Paul decided to dig out Lake Michigan so he could have a water bowl his own size. Between which two states is Lake Michigan? ______________________________

At Home: Ask students to name the states on the map not mentioned in the questions above.

Name______________________________ Date______________ **Practice 100**

Story Elements

Understanding what the **characters** in a story do as well as where they do it helps us to understand what the story is about.

Answer the following questions.

1. Where are Cookie, Cowgirl Pam, Cowboy Sam, and the cowhands?

____

____

2. Why do Sam and Pam have time to tell the story of Pecos Bill?

____

____

3. Why was Bill's family always moving?

____

____

4. How did Pecos Bill get his name?

____

____

5. How did Bill invent the lasso?

____

____

6. How did Pecos Bill first meet Slue-Foot Sue?

____

____

At Home: Have students organize their answers in a three-column chart. Have them label the columns as follows: Character, Setting, Plot.

Name________________________ Date______________ **Practice 101**

Make Inferences

Sometimes a character in a story doesn't say exactly how he or she feels about something. Readers must then **infer** how the character feels by thinking about what the character says or does, or how he or she acts.

Read the sentences below. Then, in the right column, write down how the character feels.

What Character Says or Does	How Character Feels
1. "No, I am not mad!" Michael yelled, angrily waving his fists in the air.	______________________ ______________________
2. "Kate!" Samantha shouted. "I can't believe you're finally here!" She hugged her friend tightly.	______________________ ______________________ ______________________
3. Vera said, "We should try to stay calm." Her knees were shaking and her teeth were chattering.	______________________ ______________________
4. Shane had to make lunch for himself. Then he had to clean his room. After that, he had to finish his homework. He sat down at the table with a loud groan and closed his eyes.	______________________ ______________________ ______________________

At Home: Ask students to explain an instance in their own lives when they had to make an inference.

Name________________________ Date____________ **Practice 102**

Multiple-Meaning Words

A **multiple-meaning** word has more than one meaning.

Read each sentence below. Then, match each sentence with the correct definition of the underlined word. Write the letter of the answer on the line.

_____ **1.** I am a big baseball fan.

_____ **2.** There is a fly in my soup.

_____ **3.** She tried to fix the broken table.

_____ **4.** A duck is a kind of bird.

_____ **5.** Did you see the school play? He had a big part in it.

_____ **6.** You are very kind.

_____ **7.** We put on the fan because it was hot.

_____ **8.** Birds can fly high.

_____ **9.** Lucy was in a big fix.

_____ **10.** Let's play ball!

a. a person who is very excited about something

b. nice

c. a story that is acted out on stage

d. trouble

e. a type

f. to move through the air with wings

g. a machine that moves the air

h. to repair

i. type of insect

j. to do something for fun

At Home: Have students look through the dictionary to find new multiple-meaning words.

Name________________________ Date____________ **Practice 103**

Main Idea

In a passage, the **main idea** is the most important point. **Supporting details** explain the main idea. Read the following story. Then write down the main idea and the supporting details.

Winter is my favorite time of year. In winter, I spend my days playing outside in the cold. I love to build people out of snow. I also love to ice skate. At the end of each day, I love to come out of the cold and drink hot chocolate.

Main Idea:

1. ____

____

Supporting Details:

2. ____

____

3. ____

____

4. ____

____

At Home: Have students think of a main idea for a story and three supporting details. Encourage them to write a story using this informantion.

Name________________________ Date____________ **Practice 104**

Vocabulary

Write the vocabulary word that fits in each of the sentences below.

beauty creeps furniture palace pure visitors

1. The cat ____________________ quietly toward the old sock. Does the cat think the sock is a mouse?

2. Everyone was surprised when the king and queen sold the royal ____________________. A week after that, they moved into a two-bedroom apartment.

3. My next-door neighbor had many friends. She always welcomed ____________________ into her home.

4. Mary bought the brown table. She thought it would look good with her other ____________________.

5. This water is very clean and ____________________. It comes from a spring in the mountains.

6. The ugly duckling did not know that one day it would be a bird of great ____________________.

At Home: Have students write a story about a visit to an abandoned castle using the vocabulary words.

Chills and Thrills

Some people are not happy when winter comes. They do not like the way the cold *creeps* into their clothes. Eli, however, thinks winter is *pure* joy. He loves the *beauty* of the ice on the trees. He loves the limbs of the trees without their leaves.

Eli liked making a snow *palace* out of ice and snow. One day, he tried to bring a chair into his palace. The room needed *furniture*. It also needed some *visitors*. But neither things nor people fit in Eli's tiny snow cave.

Eli didn't mind too much. His dog could fit in the cave. And with that white fur, she looked like a big, warm polar bear! Eli's dog loved winter as much as Eli did.

1. How does the cold get into people's clothes?

____

2. What kind of *furniture* did Eli try to bring to his cave?

____

3. Who could not fit in Eli's cave?

____

4. Which *visitor* could fit into Eli's cave?

____

5. How does Eli feel about the winter time?

____

At Home: Have students discuss the different things they do in each of the four seasons. Then have them draw a picture showing one of the activities for each season.

Name ______________________ Date ______________ **Practice 105**

Story Comprehension

Answer the following questions about "A Very Cool Place to Visit."

1. What parts of the hotel are made out of ice and snow? ______________

____

____

2. Why do people want to stay at the hotel? ______________

____

____

3. Name two ways that guests stay warm at the Ice Hotel.

____

____

____

____

4. What greets visitors as they arrive at the hotel? ______________

____

5. What happens each spring? ______________

____

At Home: Have students imagine that they are visiting the Ice Hotel for a night, and have them write about their experiences.

Name________________________ Date____________ **Practice 106**

Use a Map

The map of Finland below is divided into four districts: the Upland District, the Lake District, the Coastal Lowlands, and the Coastal Islands.

Write the name of the district beside the description of it.

1. This district contains many lakes. Forests cover most of the land.

 ____

2. This district is found in the far north. It has the smallest population.

 ____

3. This district contains many small islands off the coast. Many Finns have summer cottages there. ____________________________

4. This district is found along the Gulf of Bothnia and the Gulf of Finland. Most of the farms and a milder climate can be found there.

 ____

5. In which district can the capital, Helsinki, be found?

 ____

At Home: Ask students to name the country that borders Finland to its west.

Summarize

A **summary** tells the main ideas of a story.

Read the paragraphs about "A Very Cool Place to Visit." Then summarize each paragraph in one sentence.

1. At one place in Sweden, the cold is everywhere. Guests feel it in their toes, fingers, and noses. Welcome to the Ice Hotel, where the building and even some of the furniture are made of snow and ice.

   ____

   ____

2. Why would people want to stay in a hotel that was cold and frozen? A worker at the hotel, says people love the hotel for its beauty. "The white fresh snow is pure winter." She also says that people want to see the northern lights.

   ____

   ____

3. Before you get into bed, you have to warm yourself up. Doing some push-ups at bedtime will help you feel warm even before you get into bed!

   ____

   ____

4. In the springtime, when the weather gets warmer, the hotel melts. When winter returns, a new building is built from fresh snow and ice. And once again, the Ice Hotel welcomes everyone into its cold and wintry world.

   ____

   ____

At Home: Have students summarize "A Very Cool Place to Visit."

Name________________________ Date____________ **Practice 108**

Multiple-Meaning Words

A word with **multiple meanings** has more than one meaning. Reading the words and sentences around a word can help you choose the correct meaning.

This list has two meanings for each underlined word in the sentences below. Look at the way each underlined word is used in the sentence. Then choose the right meaning for each word from the list.

between winter and summer	or	leap
not warm	or	sickness
move in a secret way	or	a dishonest person
pieces of something hard	or	gets in the way

1. At one hotel in Sweden, the cold doesn't have to sneak in.

   ____

2. The hotel's 100 beds are made from ice blocks covered with reindeer skins. ______________________________

3. Each spring, when the weather warms up, the hotel melts.

   ____

4. Once again, the Ice Hotel is ready to welcome people into the cold.

   ____

At Home: Have students find a multiple-meaning word in a newspaper or magazine article.

Name______________________ Date______________ **Practice** 109

Context Clues

Context clues are words before or after an unfamiliar word that help us to understand its meaning.

Circle the context clues in each sentence that help you to figure out the meaning of the word in dark type. Then write a possible definition for the word.

1. Nothing grew from this **barren** land.

   barren: ______________________________

2. The girls ate the **entire** pie, and there wasn't even a crumb left.

   entire: ______________________________

3. He **improved** the garden when he made better paths through the roses.

   improved: ______________________________

4. Grandma tells many tales and **legends** about our ancestors.

   legends: ______________________________

5. The angry **scowl** on your face makes you look very unhappy.

   scowl: ______________________________

6. The **antique** clock was from a time long ago.

   antique: ______________________________

At Home: Ask students to compare their definitions with the ones in the dictionary.

Name________________________________ Date______________ **Practice 110**

Unit 3 Vocabulary Review

A. Supply the correct word from the box.

orchestra	concert	imaginary	conductor	musician

Helen pretended she was the ________________ of an ________________. She could hear the ________________ music in her head. When she waved her arms, each ________________ played faster. The pretend audience clapped wildly. At the end of the ________________, they threw her flowers.

B. Read each word in Column 1. Then find a word in Column 2 that means the opposite. Write the letter of the word on the line.

1. shallow _____	**a.** bright
2. ill _____	**b.** cellar
3. miserable _____	**c.** deep
4. faded _____	**d.** lost
5. attic _____	**e.** well
6. stumbled _____	**f.** happy
7. located _____	**g.** leaped

At Home: Have students write a story that uses the vocabulary words in Part B.

Name________________________________ Date______________ **Practice 111**

Unit 3 Vocabulary Review

A. Answer the questions. Then explain each answer by writing what the vocabulary word means.

1. Which is more likely to have a pattern on it, a star or a sweater?

____

____

2. Would you find blossoms on a tree or on a bird? ______________

____

3. What would you do at dawn, wake up or eat lunch? ______________

____

4. Which would you combine, a fried egg and milk or bread and butter?

____

5. Which would you find in the wilderness, a deer or a grocery store?

____

B. Label each column with a word from the box below.

costume	furniture	instrument

______________	______________	______________
bed	sailor	piano
chair	scarecrow	horn
table	magician	drum

At Home: Have students make lists like the ones in Part B that name things you could find in the wilderness.

Sequence of Events

In a story, events take place in a certain order, or **sequence.**

Read the two sets of events below. They are out of order. Number each event in its proper order.

Set A

_____ Luis got back up and said, "Dad, I hurt my knee."

_____ "Ouch," Luis yelled, and tried to get back up.

_____ Luis fell down and hurt his knee.

_____ Luis tripped over a rock.

_____ Luis and his father went outside for a walk.

Set B

_____ Luis's knee felt better.

_____ Luis's father said, "I think it's just a scratch. Let's go home and take care of it."

_____ Luis's father came up to him and looked at his knee.

_____ Luis's father put a bandage on his knee.

_____ Luis and his father carefully washed the knee with soap and water.

At Home: Have students list the sequence of events from a recent newspaper story or television show.

Name ______________________ Date ____________ **Practice 113**

Vocabulary

Answer **true** or **false** to each statement. Explain the false statements.

1. When you have *completely* finished your chores, it means that you have nothing left to do. ______________________

____

2. Dogs, cats, and elephants are good examples of *humans*. ____________

____

3. Breakfast, lunch, and dinner are different *meals* that we eat during the day. ______________________

____

4. When a car is moving, it is in *motion*. ______________________

____

5. An answer to a question is known as a *reply*. ______________________

____

6. To find out someone's *weight*, you need a measuring tape. ____________

____

At Home: Have students write a paragraph describing their favorite meal.

THE WORLD OF YES

At night it is usually *completely* dark. You can barely see anything. That is, unless there is a full moon.

Most *humans* are asleep during the night. But many animals spend the night in a constant state of *motion*. This is feeding time, the time for munching and crunching.

Some animals are known to eat more than their own *weight* in food—each and every night! What would you say if someone asked whether or not you could do the same thing? "Impossible!" you'd probably *reply*. "That is too big a *meal* for me!"

For the many animals that feed at night, the more snacks they find, the better sleep they'll have ... during the day!

1. What is another way of saying *answer*?

___

2. What is another word for *people*?

___

3. Being "on the go" means being in what kind of state?

___

4. At night some animals eat this.

___

5. Why do you think some animals feed at night?

At Home: Ask students what types of animals might forage for food at night.

Name______________________ Date____________ **Practice 114**

Story Comprehension

Think about what happens in "The Terrible EEK"
Then complete the summary below.

Beginning

One rainy night in **(1)** ______________________ long ago, a father tells his son that he is most afraid of **(2)** ______________________.
A **(3)** __________ thinks he hears a "terrible eek." A **(4)** __________ doesn't know what a terrible leak is. Both the thief and the wolf think the father is talking about **(5)** ______________________. When the thief falls on the wolf, both are **(6)** ______________________. Each of them thinks **(7)** ______________________ is the "terrible eek."

Middle

After the thief **(8)** ______________________, the wolf returns to **(9)** ______________________. The wolf asks the tiger **(10)** ______________________ ______________________. They go to **(11)** ______________________ where the thief fell. A monkey goes too.

End

The monkey pulls **(12)** ______________________ out of the hole with his tail. By now, they all are so frightened that **(13)** ______________________ ______________________ Meanwhile, the boy and his father are **(14)** ______________________ in their beds.

At Home: Have students underline the setting and circle the characters in their summaries.

Name ______________________ Date __________ **Practice 115**

Use a Chart

A **chart** arranges facts and figures in an easy-to-read layout. Fill in the chart by using the information in the sentences below.

1. At Mountain School, they had 56 days of rainfall.
2. At Valley School, they had 67 inches of snow.
3. At Coastal School, they measured 85 inches of rain.
4. At Inland School, they had only 2 total days of snowfall.
5. The smallest amount of snow was 8 inches and it fell at the Inland School.

Reported Rainfall and Snowfall At Area Grade Schools in One Year

School	Rain (in inches)	Snow (in inches)	Total Days of Rainfall	Total Days of Snowfall
Mountain School	21	120	____	39
____________	11	67	43	33
Coastal School	____	12	101	4
Inland School	4	____	21	____

At Home: Have students search through newspapers for a weather chart and cut it out.

Name________________________ Date______________ **Practice 116**

Sequence of Events

In a story, events take place in a certain **sequence**, or order.

Read the events below from "The Terrible EEK" The events are listed out of order. Write the events in order.

The thief landed on the back of the wolf.
The wolf ran into the woods.
"Father, are you ever afraid?" the boy asked.
The thief grabbed a branch.
The thief fell into a hole.
The wolf asked the tiger for help.
The father told the boy that he was most afraid of a terrible leak.
The branch broke.

1. ______________________________
2. ______________________________
3. ______________________________
4. ______________________________
5. ______________________________
6. ______________________________
7. ______________________________
8. ______________________________

At Home: Have students write two more story events in the proper places on their lists.

Name______________________ Date__________ **Practice 117**

Form Generalizations

A generalization is a broad statement that is based on examples.

Think of some things you have heard about animals. Write a generalization about each animal.

1. dog

____

2. cat

____

3. mouse

____

4. parrot

____

5. elephant

____

6. cricket

____

At Home: Have students write two generalizations about sheep.

Name________________________ Date__________ **Practice 118**

Suffixes

A **suffix** is a word part that can be added to the end of a word. Adding a suffix creates a new word with its own meaning. Sometimes the spelling of the base word changes when a suffix is added. Some common suffixes include:

-y ("full of" or "having") **-ly** ("in a certain manner")

In each of the following sentences, circle the suffix in the underlined word. Then write a new sentence, replacing the underlined word with a phrase that has the same meaning. For example, replace the underlined word sunny with the phrase *full of sun.*

1. She smiled sweetly at me.

____

2. He speaks very quietly.

____

3. Yesterday it was rainy .

____

4. I wish the sky were not so cloudy.

____

5. The children smiled happily at one another.

____

____

6. He looked at me strangely.

____

At Home: Have students write two lists of words. One should have words that end with *-ly*; the other should have words that end with *-y*.

Name ______________________ Date ____________ **Practice 119**

Author's Purpose, Point of View

Here are three common purposes or reasons why authors write: to **inform**, or to give readers facts; to **persuade**, or to convince readers to believe or do something; to **entertain**, or to tell a good story.

Read each passage. On the first line following each passage, write one of the three purposes described in bold type above to explain why the author wrote the passage. On the second line, write the author's **point of view**, the way he or she feels about the story.

Art class should be an hour long, not half an hour. Right now, we never have enough time to finish our work. If art class were longer, we would work better and learn more. Art is a very important class. We should take it seriously.

1. Purpose: ______________________________

2. Point of view: ______________________________

I love knock-knock jokes. Listen to this one: "Knock, knock!" "Who's there?" "Boo." "Boo who?" "Why are you crying?"

3. Purpose: ______________________________

4. Point of view: ______________________________

There are five different schools in my town. About 500 students go to each school. There are three grade schools, one junior high school, and one high school. This year I still go to grade school. Next year I will go to junior high school. I can't wait!

5. Purpose: ______________________________

6. Point of view: ______________________________

____

At Home: Have students add a few sentences to one of the passages above, keeping the same purpose.

Vocabulary

Supply the correct words from the list. The same vocabulary word is used twice in each example.

members	dozens	comforting
relatives	encouraging	designed

1. We had to bake ________________ of cookies to feed everyone who came to the meeting. A dozen is a group of twelve. The word ________________ is used to describe large numbers of things.

2. My piano teacher kept ________________ me to practice until I finally learned the new song. If you are ________________ people, you are giving them hope and the courage to get things done.

3. Last week, our club welcomed seven new ________________. People who belong to a group such as a team or a family are known as ________________.

4. During the holidays my grandparents and a few other ________________ come for dinner. ________________ are people in the same family.

5. The nurse was feeding and ________________ her patients to help them get well. ________________ people means trying to make them feel better.

6. Jack's sister ________________ a new coat for herself. When something is ________________, it is planned, drawn, or outlined.

At Home: Have students design an article of clothing that they would like to wear. They can draw a picture, or they can cut out a design on colored paper.

Happy, Happy Birthday!

The Fourth of July is a special day at Jake's house. All of his *relatives* come to visit. The *members* of Jake's family have a great big birthday party for two. It is Jake's birthday and the birthday of the United States.

At the party, Jake's father cooks *dozens* of hamburgers on a grill. There is always someone next to the grill *encouraging* him to make more.

Dessert is always fun. Everyone eats the birthday cake that Jake's mother has *designed*. It has a red, white, and blue flag.

Jake finds it *comforting* that he and his country have the same birthday. He will always have a special friend on his special day—the United States!

1. What were people *encouraging* Jake's father to do?

____

2. What is another name for cousins, aunts, uncles, and grandparents?

____

3. Who *designed* the cake?

____

4. What does Jake find *comforting*?

____

5. Who were celebrating together in the story?

____

At Home: Have students design on paper cakes to celebrate a holiday of their choice.

Name________________________________ Date______________ **Practice 121**

Story Comprehension

Answer these questions about "In My Family."

1. Why would the mother and grandmother be angry with the children?

____

____

2. What did Arturo try to feed to the toad?

____

3. What is the grandfather's name?

____

4. Who is watching the grandfather work?

____

5. Why is there no place to sit in Aunt Paz and Uncle Beto's house?

____

____

6. Who made Mary Jane's birthday cake?

____

7. Where do people dance in the summer?

____

8. Who taught Carmen how to dance?

____

At Home: Have students write a few sentences explaining what dance means to Carmen.

Name ______________________ Date ____________ **Practice 122**

Use a Diagram

Fill in the blanks in the diagram with the name or dates for the underlined family member.

1. The life span of Dorothy Ray was 1895–1966.

2. Lester Mills is a child of George Mills.

3. Cathy Moss married Oliver Mills.

4. Vicky is one of Sara Mills and Paul Wilson's three children.

5. Emma Penn married Kevin Mills.

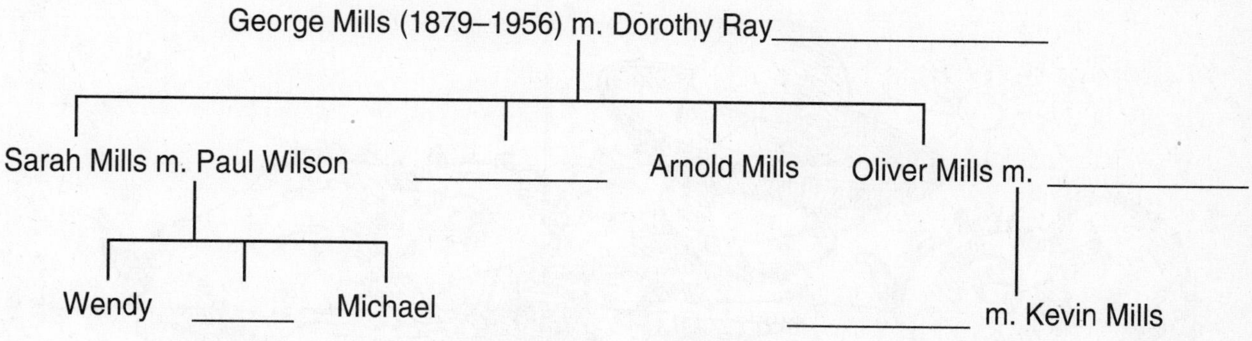

George Mills (1879–1956) m. Dorothy Ray ______________

Sarah Mills m. Paul Wilson | ____________ | Arnold Mills | Oliver Mills m. ____________

Wendy ______ Michael

____________ m. Kevin Mills

McGraw-Hill School Division

At Home: Have students try to write a family tree diagram for their family.

Name________________________ Date____________ **Practice 123**

Author's Purpose, Point of View

Sometimes an author has more than one purpose in telling a story. What purposes do you think the author had for writing "In My Family"? Answer each question below.

Did you enjoy the story? Tell two things about the story that entertained you.

1. ____

2. ____

What did you learn as you read the story? Tell three things that you learned by reading "In My Family."

3. ____

4. ____

5. ____

What do you think is the author's point of view about her family?

6. ____

____

At Home: Have students write a paragraph that informs the reader. The paragraph may be about their family, if they wish.

Name________________________________ Date______________ **Practice 124**

Sequence of Events

Events in a story happen in a certain **sequence**, or order.

Read the events below. They are out of order. Use the boxes to draw the events in order.

Mary's mother said, "Thank you," and gave her a hug.

Mary gave the card to her mother.

Mary drew balloons on the card and wrote, "Happy Mother's Day, Mom!"

Mary got paper, crayons, and a card.

At Home: Have students write four events in sequence.

Name______________________________ Date____________ **Practice 125**

Figurative Language

Have you ever heard someone say, "It's raining cats and dogs"? Of course, cats and dogs aren't really falling from the sky. But this exaggeration gets across the idea of heavy rain in a colorful way. Imaginative phrases such as this are called **figurative language.**

A **simile** is a type of figurative language that makes a comparison using the word **like** or **as**. The following sentence is an example of a simile. He was as tall as a giant.

Read each pair of sentences. Write **S** next to the one that is an example of a simile.

1. _____ I like to draw the lake.

_____ The lake is as shiny as a piece of glass.

2. _____ The chair was as hard as a rock.

_____ The chair was too small for me.

3. _____ Carmen has fun looking at the toads.

_____ Carmen is as free of cares as a toad.

4. _____ His hands felt as cold as ice.

_____ He put his hands in his pockets.

5. _____ He is as quiet as a mouse.

_____ He never talks to anyone.

6. _____ The cat was as round as a ball.

_____ The cat was small and round.

At Home: Ask students to circle the figurative language in each sentence they chose.

Name________________________ Date____________ **Practice 126**

Cause and Effect

A **cause** is the reason something happened. An **effect** is what happened.

Read each pair of sentences below.
Write *cause* next to each sentence that explains why something happened.
Write *effect* next to those that tell what happened.

1. Max was afraid. ____________
2. Max screamed. ____________

3. Terence ate dinner. ____________
4. Terence felt hungry. ____________

5. Everything was covered in snow. ____________
6. Snow fell all night. ____________

7. Otto had a cold. ____________
8. Otto stayed home from school. ____________

9. Gregory woke up late. ____________
10. Gregory was late to school. ____________

11. Mary studied hard. ____________
12. Mary did well on the test. ____________

 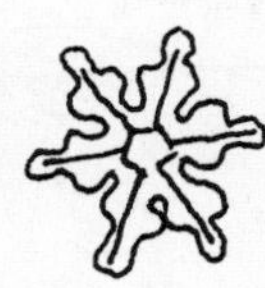   

At Home: Have students write one more pair of sentences showing cause and effect.

Name________________________ Date____________ **Practice 127**

Vocabulary

Complete each sentence with a word from the list below.

discovered	insects	remains
ribs	tough	treat

1. Birds like to eat tiny ________________ that live on leaves.
2. You could find the ________________, or what is left behind, of a fallen cactus lying on the desert floor.
3. Wooden ________________, like the bony ones in your chest, hold up a giant cactus from the inside.
4. The walls of a woodpecker's home inside a cactus are ________________ not weak.
5. Nectar is a delicious ________________ that a bird might find in a cactus flower.
6. An owl ________________, or found, an empty hole in a cactus and decided to live there.

At Home: Have students write a new sentence for each of the vocabulary words.

Treasures on the Beach

It was Sunday. There was no school and I was walking on the beach. The birds were so far away they looked like tiny *insects*.

As I walked I *discovered* the *remains* of an old ship. Most of it had washed away. But some of its wooden *ribs* were still sticking out of the sand. The wood looked smooth and *tough*.

Inside the ship was a treasure chest. Inside the great box were many beautiful things. There were beautiful clothes and lots of jewelry. One thing really caught my eye. It was a big shining ring. What a *treat*!

Then, just as I was about to put on the ring, a bird swooped down and grabbed it! Oh well. At least I had a nice walk on the beach.

1. What was *discovered* by the speaker?

___

2. What was the *treat* that was found?

___

3. What words describe the ship's wooden *ribs*?

___

4. What did the birds in the sky look like?

___

5. Why was the speaker not very upset about losing the ring?

___

At Home: Ask the students how their *ribs* are like the ribs of the ship in the story. How are they different?

Name________________________ Date__________ **Practice 128**

Story Comprehension

The saguaro cactus has a very long life!

Add details from "Cactus Hotel." Tell what the cactus looks like and what animals are found on or near the cactus at each stage of its growth.

Years Old	Details
10	
25	
50	
60	
150	
200	

At Home: Have students draw a picture of what the saguaro cactus looks like after 150 years.

Name________________________ Date______________ **Practice 129**

Use a Chart

Read the story below. It contains many facts that could be shown in a chart.

> **Mammals of the Southwest**
>
> Many different animals live in the Southwestern states. Some of the mammals are quite different from those that live in other areas. The ringtail has a face like a fox. It is a member of the raccoon family but doesn't have a face mask. It lives among rocks and boulders and is gray with a whitish belly. It is about 2.5 feet long.
>
> If you saw a brown cat with a white belly and black bars on its tail, it was probably a bobcat. Bobcats are about four feet long and live in thickets or among rocks and logs.
>
> Prairie dogs live in a "town" of burrows. They're reddish brown and about fifteen inches long. Some have black tails.
>
> If you hear a terrifying scream near a cave in the mountains, it's probably a mountain lion. This seven-foot-long mammal is a yellowish brown and is also called a cougar.

Now study the chart below. Use the facts from the story to complete the charts.

Mammals of the Southwest

Animals	Length	Where They Live	Color of Animal	Special Feature
Ringtail	2.5 ft.	____________ ____________	gray with white belly	face like a fox
________	4 ft.	thickets, rocks, logs	brown with white belly	black bars on tail
Prairie dog	_____	"towns" of burrows	____________ ____________	some with black tails
Mountain lion	7 ft.	in caves in mountains	yellowish brown	____________ ____________

At Home: Ask students to look up two other desert animals and include them in the chart.

Name________________________ Date____________ **Practice 130**

Cause and Effect

Use information from "Cactus Hotel" to complete the cause-and-effect chart below.

Cause	Effects
Fruit falls from a cactus.	1. Then a rat ____________________. 2. A seed falls off of the rat's whiskers and lands ____________________.
It rains in the desert.	3. A young cactus ____________________ ____________________.
Flowers appear at the top of the cactus.	4. Birds, bees, and bats see the flowers and ____________________ ____________________.
The cactus falls down.	5. The arms of the cactus ____________________. 6. The creatures that lived high in the cactus ____________________.

At Home: Have students describe one more effect of the cactus falling.

Name________________________________ Date______________ **Practice 131**

Sequence of Events

Events in a story happen in a certain **sequence**, or order.

Read the events. For each event, write what you think might happen next.

1. Brian felt very sleepy.

____

2. The end of Natasha's pencil broke.

____

3. The class finished eating lunch.

____

4. Leslie threw the ball.

____

5. Frederico opened his present.

____

6. Amy tried out for the team.

____

7. There was a snowstorm.

____

8. I went to the mall with my dad.

____

At Home: Have students choose their favorite sequence and illustrate it.

Name______________________________ Date____________ **Practice 132**

Suffixes

Suffixes are word parts that can be added to the end of a word. Adding a suffix creates a new word with its own meaning. Sometimes the spelling of the base word changes when a suffix is added. Some common suffixes are listed below.

Some Common Suffixes

Suffix	Meaning	Example
-able	able to be	likable
-ly	in a certain manner	secretly
-y	full of	sandy

Use the chart above for examples of suffixes and their meanings. Write the correct meaning for each word below and use each word in a sentence.

1. comfortable ______________________________

____

2. juicy ___________________________________

____

3. slowly __________________________________

____

4. sharply _________________________________

____

5. deeply __________________________________

____

6. shady ___________________________________

____

At Home: Challenge students to write two sentences that include all of the words above.

Name______________________________ Date______________ **Practice 133**

Form Generalizations

Below are some generalizations. Read each carefully. Then write down two examples that would lead to the generalization stated.

1. Many animals are furry.

____

____

2. Some students bring lunch from home.

____

____

3. Many plants are green.

____

____

4. Grown men are usually taller than grown women.

____

____

At Home: Have students write two examples for the generalization, "Many games are played with a ball."

Name________________________________ Date______________ **Practice** 134

Vocabulary

Tell whether each of the following statements is **true** or **false**. If it is false, explain why.

1. Babies are older than *adults*.

____

____

2. If you *swallow* something, it goes down your throat.

____

____

3. To *feast* on something means to eat it.

____

____

4. *Mammals* breathe air.

____

____

5. When there is a storm, the sea is *calm*.

____

____

6. Two is a *vast* number of people.

____

____

At Home: For each false statement above, have students make up a true statement using the vocabulary word.

A Whale of a Mural

"Class, today we are going to learn about a new kind of *mammal*," said Miss Linder. "Remember, mammals are animals who give birth to live babies. They don't lay eggs."

"Whales are mammals," said June. "Let's make a *vast* mural to show how big they are!"

The class painted an *adult* whale with a baby whale. Both of the whales were shown in *calm* water. The adult whale had her giant mouth open to *swallow* tiny bits of food.

"You did a great job, class!" said Miss Linder. "Your whale has much food to *feast* on!"

"I worked so hard, I'm as hungry as a whale!" said June.

1. What is a fully grown person or animal?

____

2. If water is not rough, what is it?

____

3. What is another word for eating a big meal?

____

4. How do whales get food from their mouths to their stomachs?

____

5. Why might it have been a lot of work for the class to paint the mural?

____

At Home: Have students look up the italicized words from the story in the dictionary. Ask them to copy the definition of each word.

Name ______________________ Date ____________ **Practice 135**

Story Comprehension

Answer the questions below.

1. Why are there so few blue whales in the world?

____

____

2. How large are blue whales?

____

____

3. How do blue whales breathe?

____

____

4. How long can a blue whale stay under the water?

____

5. How large is the food that blue whales eat?

____

____

6. Why do blue whales grow fatter in the summer?

____

____

At Home: Have students write three more sentences describing how large a blue whale is.

Name________________________ Date____________ **Practice 136**

Use a Graph

The bar graph below shows different types of whales in the world. Use the graph to help you answer the questions that follow.

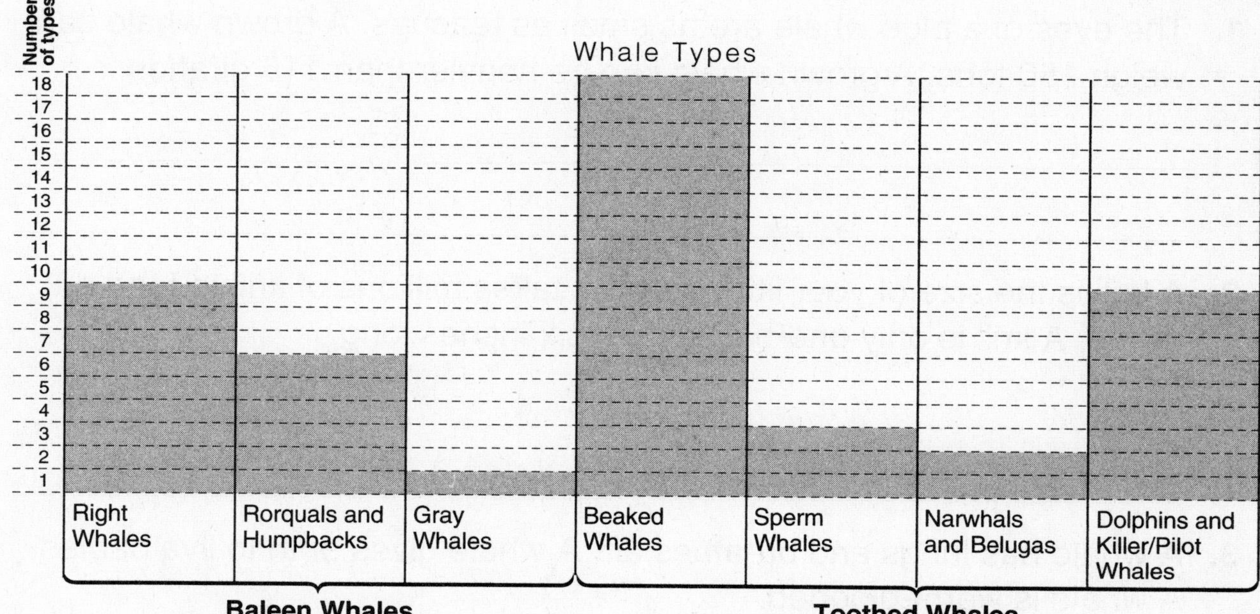

1. Which group of whales contains the largest number of types?

____

2. How many types of gray whale are there?

____

3. Is a beaked whale a baleen whale or a toothed whale?

____

4. What are the types of baleen whales?

____

5. How many different types of sperm whales are there?

____

At Home: Have students choose a whale, draw its picture, and write three sentences about it.

Name______________________ Date__________ **Practice 137**

Form Generalizations

Read the groups of facts below. Make a generalization based on each group.

1. The eyes of a blue whale are as small as teacups. A grown whale can weigh 150 tons. A grown whale can be heavier than 115 giraffes.

____

____

2. A krill is the size of your little finger. It takes millions of krill to feed a whale. A krill is only one-half inch to six inches long.

____

____

3. A whale has lungs and breathes air. A whale gives birth to live babies. A whale is warm-blooded.

____

____

4. Because there isn't much light in deep water, it's hard to see. Whales have to use their sense of hearing and their sense of touch to find their way in deep water.

____

____

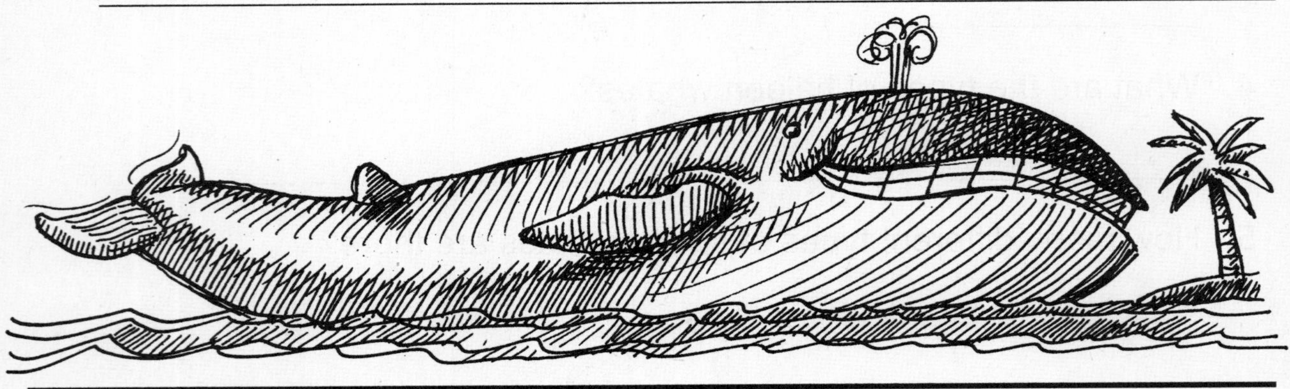

At Home: Have students write one more generalization about blue whales.

Author's Purpose, Point of View

Read each passage. Is the author trying to **entertain** us, **inform** us of facts, or **persuade** us to do something? Write the author's purpose. Then explain your answer.

> Dear Principal,
>
> Our school needs a new gym. The one we have now is too small. During gym class, it gets very crowded in there.
>
> Thank you very much.
>
> Yours,
>
> Genelle Williams

1. I think the author wants to ____________________

2. Reason: ____

____

Once upon a time, there lived a princess. Well, not exactly a princess. Once upon a time, there lived a little girl who really wanted to be a princess. Every day, the little girl said, "Oh, I would give anything to be a princess."

3. I think the author wants to ____________________

4. Reason: ____

____

My school has three hundred children and twenty teachers. It is for children in grades five through eight.

5. I think the author wants to ____________________

6. Reason: ____

____

At Home: Have students write a paragraph to persuade the reader about something.

Figurative Language

Colorful words and phrases are called **figurative language**.

One type of figurative language is the **simile**. A simile is a comparison that uses the word **like** or **as**. Here is an example of a simile. The bush was as tall as an elephant.

Another type of figurative language is a **metaphor**. A metaphor is a comparison that does not use the word **like** or **as**. Here's an example of a metaphor. The line snaked through the street.

Read each sentence. Underline the figurative language. On the line beneath, write the meaning of the sentence.

1. We felt the cold breath of winter on our cheeks.

____

2. He heard the leaves on the trees whispering.

____

____

3. The ear of a blue whale is as small as the end of a pencil.

____

____

4. The blow of a whale is as high as a house.

____

____

5. When a blue whale eats, its throat opens out like a huge balloon.

____

____

At Home: Have students tell whether the figurative language that they underlined in each example above is a simile or a metaphor.

Name ______________________ Date ____________ **Practice 140**

Cause and Effect

Write four possible effects for each cause below.

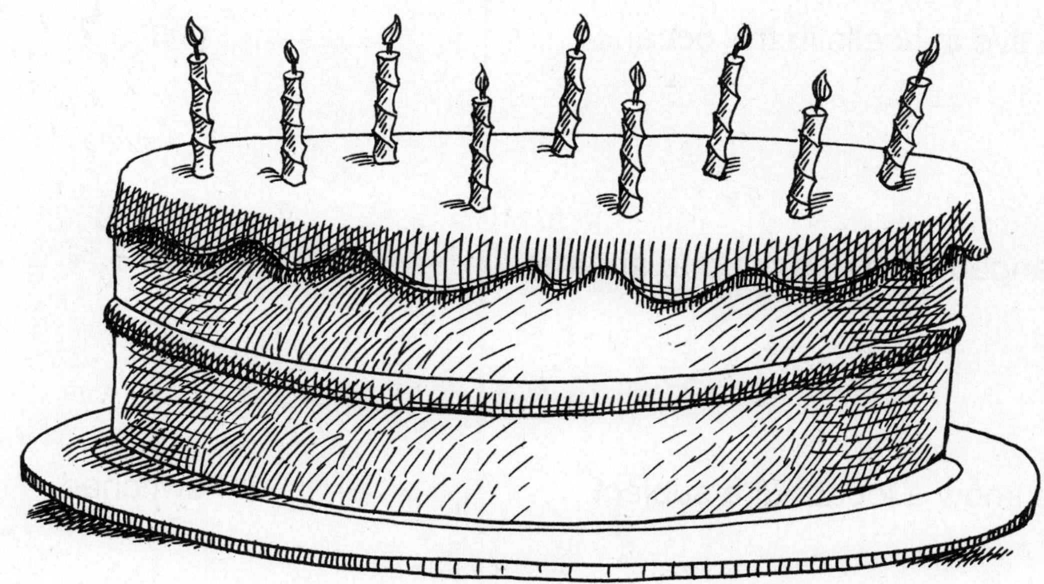

Cause: It is a sunny day.

Effects:

1. ______________________________

____

2. ______________________________

____

3. ______________________________

____

4. ______________________________

____

Cause: It is my birthday.

Effects:

5. ______________________________

____

6. ______________________________

____

7. ______________________________

____

8. ______________________________

____

At Home: Have students write two effects for the cause "I joined the baseball team."

Vocabulary

Draw a line from each clue to the word it describes.

1. We live in shells in the ocean.	gain
2. changed from one thing to another	clams
3. We know a lot about a subject.	switched
4. This happens when we increase something.	compared
5. How were things the same? How were they different?	experts
6. made into fine, tiny bits	powdered

At Home: Challenge students to use the vocabulary words in sentences.

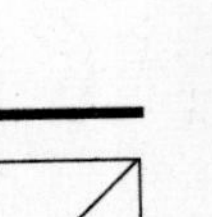

A Clammy Tale

Once there were two clams. Both *clams* thought they were *experts* at keeping their shells shiny. Every day they *compared* their shells to see whose shined more in the sun.

One day the clams woke up to find that their shells were not shiny at all. They were covered with *powdered* white stuff. Neither had ever seen the white dust before. It was falling from the sky.

The snow was very heavy on the clams' shells. They didn't want to *gain* a lot of weight. "If I *switched* places with those seagulls," one clam shouted, "I wouldn't have this heavy white powder all over me."

"Yes," said the other clam, "but they don't carry around their own house either. We don't have it that bad!"

1. At the beginning of the story, how did the clams pass their time?

____

2. What did the clams think they were *experts* at doing?

____

3. What was falling from the clouds?

____

4. What is a word that describes the white stuff on the clams' shells?

____

5. What birds did the clams talk about?

____

At Home: Ask students to think of other animals that carry around their own home.

Name________________________ Date____________ **Practice 142**

Story Comprehension

Answer these questions about "J.J.'s Big Day."

1. What kind of whale is J.J.?

2. How old was J.J. when she washed up on the beach?

3. What did J.J. drink instead of a mother whale's milk?

4. What were the two problems with returning J.J. to the ocean?

5. How did the scientists move J.J. back to the ocean?

At Home: Have students write a paragraph describing J.J.'s first day back in the ocean.

Name________________________________ Date______________ **Practice 143**

Use a Graph

These two graphs show how fishing for whales has changed over the years. The first graph shows that the number of whale hunters and their ships has changed over time. The second graph shows the numbers of whales hunted at three different times.

In the 1980s, almost all hunting for whales was stopped. Now the number of whales in the oceans is increasing again.

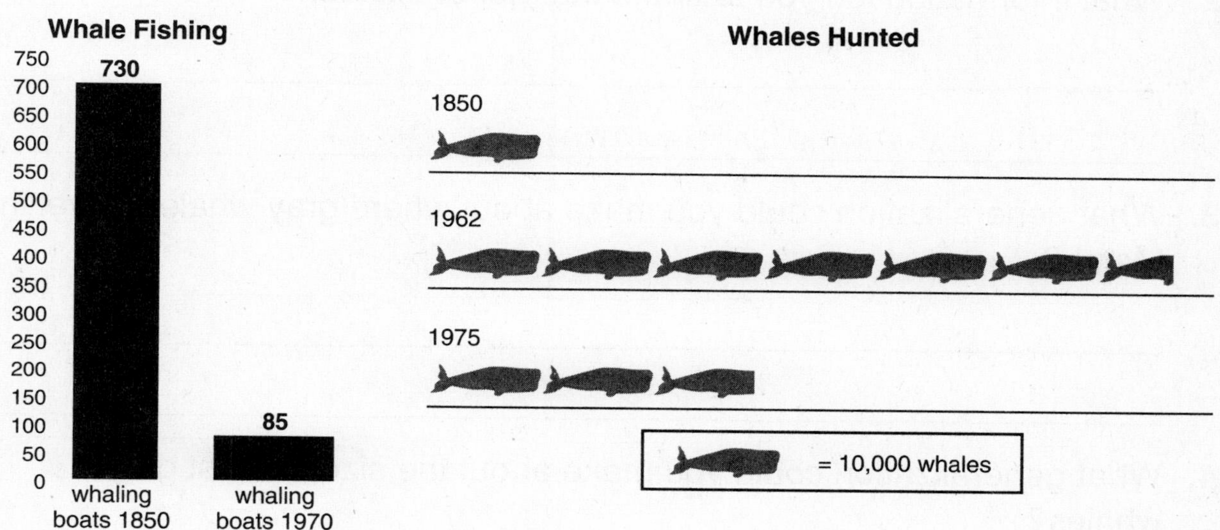

Use the graphs above to answer these questions. **True or False:**

1. The number of whaling boats increased from 1850 to 1970. __________
2. The number of whales captured in the 1970s decreased greatly from the number captured in the 1960s. __________
3. One symbol of a whale stands for 10,000 whales. __________
4. If the symbol of the whale is cut in half, it means only half the whale was caught. __________

At Home: Have students read the chart and write a sentence describing how whale hunting changed from 1850 to 1975.

Name_______________________ Date_____________ **Practice 144**

Form Generalizations

Use the information in "J.J.'s Big Day" to answer the questions below.

1. What generalization could you make about how fast whales grow?

____

____

2. What information led you to make that generalization?

____

____

3. What generalization could you make about where gray whales travel in March?

____

____

4. What generalization could you make about the size of most gray whales?

____

____

5. What information led you to make that generalization?

____

____

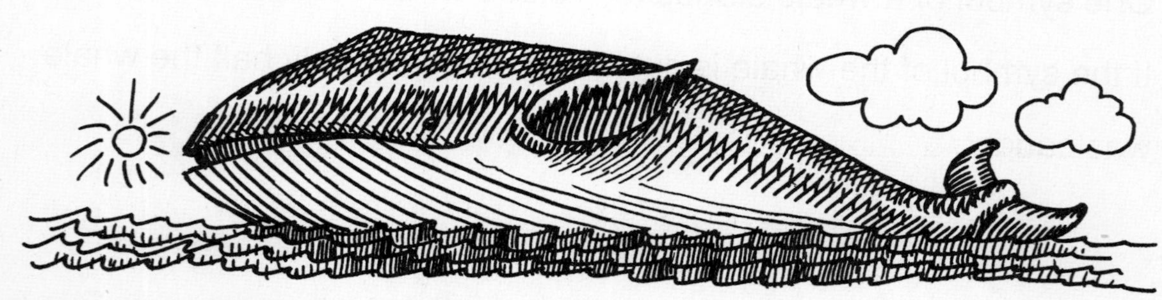

At Home: Have students write a generalization about what gray whales eat, and explain the information that led them to make that generalization.

Name________________________ Date____________ **Practice 145**

Figurative Language

Similes use the words **like** or **as** to compare one subject to another. **Metaphors** also make comparisons, but without using the words **like** or **as**.

Write **Simile**, **Metaphor**, or **Neither** to describe each sentence.

1. I am as hungry as a horse. ________________
2. His eyes are shining diamonds. ________________
3. That dish smells good. ________________
4. I looked out at the ocean of people. ________________
5. My skin is as smooth as silk. ________________
6. Johnny laughed on his way home. ________________
7. Annie is as happy as a clam. ________________
8. Paul cried a flood of tears. ________________
9. All the animals were hungry. ________________
10. The bear was green with envy. ________________
11. My cat is as big as a house. ________________
12. Fishing is more fun than digging. ________________

At Home: Give students three subjects, such as a man dancing, a newly hatched chick, and a girl running a race. Ask students to write similes or metaphors that describe each subject.

Suffixes

Adding a **suffix** to a word can change its meaning.
The attic is full of dust.

dust + y = dusty

The attic is **dusty**.

Write the underlined word. Then add the suffix to the underlined word to make a new word.

Rewrite the sentence with the new word.

1. These socks smell.

    ____________ + y = ____________

    ____

2. I can wear this shirt.

    ____________ + able = ____________

    ____

3. The boy plays quiet music.

    ____________ + ly = ____________

    ____

4. I can read this book.

    ____________ + able = ____________

    ____

5. The honey sticks to me.

    ____________ + y = ____________

    ____

At Home: Ask students to illustrate one of the sentences they wrote.

Name________________________ Date____________ **Practice 147**

Unit 1 Vocabulary Review

A. Answer each question.

1. **feast** When would people have a feast? ____________________

____

2. **reply** If you wrote a reply to an invitation, what did you do? ________

____

3. **experts** How do people become experts? ____________________

____

4. **treat** If someone wanted to give you a treat, what would you ask for?

____

B. Answer each question with a word from the box.

clams	adult	dozens	comforting	gain	meal

1. Which word means the same as grown-up? ____________________
2. Which word means the opposite of lose? ____________________
3. Which word could you use instead of breakfast, lunch, or dinner?

   ____

4. Which word lets you know that there are many of something?

   ____

5. Which word means making someone feel better? ____________________
6. Which word names things that live in the water? ____________________

At Home: Have students write a paragraph that uses the vocabulary words in Part A.

Name____________________ Date__________ **Practice 148**

Unit 1 Vocabulary Review

A. Supply the correct vocabulary word from the box.

relatives	encouraging	swallow

1. Sam's teacher is always ________________ him to read more.
2. Mimi's cousins were the only ________________ at the party.
3. Chew your food well before you ________________ it.

B. Use words from the list to complete the sentences, then finish the crossword puzzle.

members	discovered	vast	compared	ribs

DOWN

1. ________________ belong to a club.
3. Leah ________________ the two books, then chose one.

ACROSS

2. If you found something new, you ________________ it.
4. The cloth of an umbrella is held in place by its ________________.
5. Something that is very, very large is ________________.

At Home: Have students write clues they could use in a crossword puzzle for the vocabulary words in Part A.

Judgments and Decisions

You make a **judgment** or **decision** based on reasons. There may be reasons both for and against something.

Read the story. List reasons for and against. Then answer the questions.

Dan and his dog spent many afternoons playing ball. Scout could chase and catch a ball almost as fast as Dan could throw one. One day while they were playing in the front yard, Scout barked at a little girl who was riding her bike. The girl was scared and began to cry. Dan's father said that from now on, Dan had to play with Scout inside the fence in the back yard. Dan was unhappy, because there was more room for Scout to chase the ball in the front of the house.

1. Reasons for keeping Scout in the backyard: ____________________

____

2. Reasons for letting Scout play in the front yard: ____________________

____

3. What do you think of the decision Dan's father made?

____

If Dan trains his dog not to bark at children and to stop running when he says the word "Sit," should Dan's father decide to let Dan and Scout play in the front yard?

4. Reasons for: ____________________

____

5. Reasons against: ____________________

____

At Home: Have students list reasons for and against a personal decision they are trying to make.

Name________________________ Date____________ **Practice 150**

Vocabulary

Write the correct word from the box to complete each sentence.

claws	delighted	disguised	furious	paced	route

1. I went to the party ______________ as a pirate.

2. The lion was ______________ when he saw that he was trapped.

3. I was ______________ when he gave me a new bike.

4. The worried man ______________ up and down the room.

5. Shall we bike along the main road or take the shorter ______________?

6. My cat has sharp ______________.

At Home: Have students draw pictures of their own faces illustrating the meanings of the words *delighted* and *furious*.

The Trackers

Chad and his father took the same *route* through the woods every day. Chad's father was teaching him about the woods. One day, they came to a tree with strange marks on it.

"Are these marks made by a wolf's *claws*?" Chad asked.

Chad was correct. His father was *delighted* that he was learning about the woods. They walked on. But Chad stopped.

"The leaves are broken," he said. "Something big *paced* through here."

Suddenly, they heard a loud and *furious* sound. Chad and his father covered themselves with branches. Then they moved safely and quickly through the woods *disguised* as trees.

1. What is another word for a path or way to go through the woods?

____

2. What are a wolf's sharp nails called?

____

3. How did Chad's father feel about him learning about the woods?

____

4. What had an animal done over the broken leaves?

____

5. Why were Chad and his father *disguised*?

At Home: Have students use each of the italicized words from the story in a sentence.

Story Comprehension

Think about "Lon Po Po." Then complete each sentence in the story map below.

When and Where
The story takes place **(1.)** ______________________, somewhere in the country of **(2.)** ______________________.
Characters
The five characters are **(3.)** ______________________ ______________________.
Story Problem
The wolf wants to **(4.)** ______________________. To keep safe, the children must **(5.)** ______________________ ______________________.
Story Events
The wolf tricks the children by **(6.)** ______________________. The children trick the wolf by **(7.)** ______________________ ______________________
How the Problem Is Solved
The wolf **(8.)** ______________________ ______________________.

At Home: Have students draw a picture for one of their answers.

Name________________________________ Date______________ **Practice 152**

Read a Newspaper

Read the newspaper story below. Try to decide which statements are opinions.

Alien Craft Lands at Old Faithful?

Donna Eggerton — Aug. 8, 1999: Wolves may not be the only returning visitors to Yellowstone National Park. Campers in the park reported strange sounds and lights last night.

"The roar was like a thousand waterfalls," Pearl Johnson explained. "We were camping by the lake. The lights seemed bigger than any spotlights I ever saw."

Last year, hikers in the area reported similar lights and noises. Many rangers felt that city people aren't used to the sights and sounds of the woods at night. "A car's headlights across the lake can look odd," one reported. "And animals in the dark make what may seem like a lot of strange noises."

A nearby Air Force base spokesman said no unidentified flying objects were in the area.

Write each sentence that contains an opinion on the lines. Consider the headline, byline, and quotations.

1. ____

2. ____

____

 3. ____

 4. ____

____

 5. ____

 6. ____

____

At Home: Have students search a newspaper for a story with opinions and cut it out.

Judgments and Decisions

Readers often make judgments about a character's actions. When you make a **judgment,** you decide what you think based on reasons you find in the story.

Read the actions of the characters below and make a judgment about the characters' actions. Then list your reasons.

In "Lon Po Po," the wolf thought he would be able to trick the children by disguising himself as their grandmother.

1. Do you think the wolf was clever? ____________________

List two reasons.

2. ____

____

3. ____

____

____

Shang decides on a way to trick the wolf. She gets her sisters to help.

4. Do you think Shang made a good decision? ____________________

List two reasons.

5. ____

6. ____

At Home: Have students tell how the sisters in "Lon Po Po" first made a bad decision, and then tell how they made a good decision.

Name_________________________ Date_____________ **Practice 154**

Summarize

When you **summarize** a story, you tell only the most important things that happen. You can also summarize the information in a paragraph.

Summarize each paragraph below in one sentence.

Alice threw away her peach in the trash, but Sam had another idea. He planted the peach pit in the ground. He knew that the seed of the plant was inside the pit. With any luck, the old peach would grow into a tree and produce hundreds of peaches in just a few years.

Summary ____

____

Some people like to train dogs; other people like to train plants! It is fun to make shapes out of growing things. People can train plants into the shape of a ball, a tree, or even an animal like a deer. All it takes to train a plant is time and patience.

Summary ____

____

At Home: Ask students to summarize what they did last summer.

Context Clues

There are two kinds of **context clues. General clues** are nearby words. Actual definitions or descriptions of the word in question are called **specific clues.**

Circle the words and phrases that help you tell what the word means. Then write the meaning of the underlined word on the line.

1. The wolf had sharp claws. They felt different from the nails on a human hand.

   ____

2. I couldn't believe I was really in the desert. It is such a hot, dry, and sandy place.

   ____

3. I didn't mean to drop the plate. It was an accident.

   ____

4. I always get names wrong. For instance, I thought that his name was John, but I was mistaken. His name is James.

   ____

5. She always tells the truth. She never tells lies.

   ____

6. He took hold of the shovel tightly with both hands. He had to grasp it or it would drop.

   ____

At Home: Have students make up context clues for nonsense words for other people to figure out.

Name________________________ Date____________ **Practice 156**

Fact and Nonfact

You can use your own knowledge to decide whether a statement is a **fact** or a **nonfact**. You can try to prove the information is a fact by looking in sources such as an atlas, an encyclopedia, a calendar, or a newspaper article.

Read each statement. Write **fact** if the statement is true. Write **nonfact** if the statement is false. Then tell how you would prove whether the statement is a fact, or a nonfact, or if you can answer from your own experience.

1. It is cold in Los Angeles and all of southern California. ____________
2. How can you prove it? ____________________________
3. No other animal in the world is as colorful as a frog. ____________
4. How can you prove it? ____________________________
5. Before people had cars, many people used horses to travel from place to place. ____________
6. How can you prove it? ____________________________
7. Many people celebrate Christmas on December 25. ____________
8. How can you prove it? ____________________________
9. Whales are the biggest animals that swim in the ocean. ____________
10. How can you prove it? ____________________________

At Home: Ask students to give you an example of a fact, and then tell how it could be proved.

Name________________________ Date____________ **Practice 157**

Vocabulary

Write the correct word from the box to complete each sentence.

rapidly	temperature	label	attack	expects	bother

1. The fighting fish started to __________________ one another.

2. She gets a lot done because she works __________________.

3. Please do not __________________ me while I am reading or cooking.

4. She knows John is a good cook, so she __________________ dinner to be delicious.

5. There was a __________________ on each sale item.

6. The __________________ must be high because I feel very hot!

At Home: Ask students to use one or two of the vocabulary words in a sentence that describes their local weather.

The Artist

Rita always drew pictures of things she saw. She also wrote a *label* for each picture. One day her brother Joe said, "Who *expects* to learn from so many pictures? Don't *bother* with all that drawing."

Rita told Joe that she learned a lot from what she drew. "Once I saw a spider *attack* a fly stuck in its web," she said. "The spider moved *rapidly* to trap the fly."

Rita also told Joe about a day when the *temperature* suddenly dropped. Everyone was slipping and sliding on the icy ground.

"My pictures help me remember," she said.

"Then draw a picture of me!" said Joe. "Then you can remember me forever."

"Yuck!" replied Rita. "How could I ever forget you!"

1. How did Rita name each picture?

____

2. What did Joe tell Rita not to *bother* doing?

____

3. How did the spider move to catch the fly?

____

4. What suddenly dropped one day?

____

5. What does Joe ask Rita to do at the end of the story?

____

At Home: Have students draw and label at least three interesting things they have seen recently.

Name ________________________ Date ______________ **Practice 158**

Story Comprehension

Think about the facts and fables you have learned about animals in "Animal Fact/Animal Fable." Then list one fact and one fable for each animal in the chart below.

Fact	Fable
turtle	
1. ____________	2. ____________
cricket	
3. ____________	4. ____________
porcupine	
5. ____________	6. ____________
dog	
7. ____________	8. ____________
ostrich	
9. ____________	10. ____________
goat	
11. ____________	12. ____________

Name____________________ Date__________ **Practice 159**

Read a Newspaper

Judge if the statements below come from a real newspaper. To do this, decide if the statements use facts about animals. If so, write **Fact** beside them. If a statement is only trying to entertain, write **Not Fact**.

1. Bats can almost see in the dark. They have radar that helps them sense objects even without seeing them. __________

2. The ostriches were so upset about the terrible weather we've been having, they hid their heads in the sand. __________

3. The goats were so bored with their meals, they ate tin cans! __________

4. The arctic tern can fly longer than any other bird. It flies over 11,000 miles without stopping. __________

5. The roadrunner bird rarely flies. When surprised, it runs across the sand at high speed. __________

6. The roadrunner bird always tricks the silly coyote, who tries to use rocket skates to catch it. __________

7. A porcupine can shoot its quills like arrows and hit a bull's-eye from 50 yards. __________

8. The quills on a porcupine are attached loosely and may shake off if it swings its tail in self-defense. __________

At Home: Have students write one sentence about birds that is a fact and one sentence that is not a fact.

Name________________________ Date______________ **Practice 160**

Fact and Nonfact

A **fact** can be proved to be true. A **nonfact** is a statement that cannot be proved. Remember that a fable is a nonfact.

Use the information you learned in "Animal Fact/Animal Fable" to complete the chart below.

Animal Fables	Animal Facts
1. Turtles ________________ ________________ ________________	2. Turtles ________________ ________________ ________________
3. Porcupines ________________ ________________ ________________	4. Porcupines ________________ ________________ ________________
5. Ostriches ________________ ________________ ________________	6. Ostriches ________________ ________________ ________________
7. Goats ________________ ________________ ________________	8. Goats ________________ ________________ ________________

At Home: Ask students to write a fact and a fable about another animal.

Summarize

When you **summarize**, you tell the most important things that happened. A summary is short and includes only the major events.

Read the story below. Then fill in the chart by writing a sentence that tells about each of the major events in the game.

The soccer game between Team Blue and Team Orange was tied 10 to 10. Andy, who was on Team Blue, ran as fast as he could and kicked the ball. He stubbed his toe, but the ball went into the net and he scored. Now the score was 11 to 10 and Team Blue was ahead.

During time-out, Andy checked his toe to make sure it wasn't hurt. When they went back to the game, Team Orange scored 4 points in a row. Now Team Orange was ahead by 3 points.

There were only a few minutes left to play when it started to rain. Then it started to pour and Mr. Wright called off the game. "We'll have to play each other again next week," he said.

Who played:	**1.** ______________________ ______________________
The score at the beginning of the story:	**2.** ______________________ ______________________
What happened right after Andy's kick:	**3.** ______________________ ______________________
How the game ended:	**4.** ______________________ ______________________ ______________________

At Home: Ask students to explain why the fact that Andy stubbed his toe is not included in the summary.

Name____________________ Date____________ **Practice 162**

Context Clues

The two types of **context clues** are **general clues**, such as nearby words and **specific clues**, such as actual definitions of the word in question.

Use context clues to figure out the meaning of the words in dark type. Write the meaning of each word in dark type on the line.

1. This kind of wood feels very **smooth**, but the other kind feels rough.

   ____

2. **September** is my favorite fall month.

   ____

3. I remember when that old dog was still a young **puppy**.

   ____

4. She can't hear you because she is **deaf**.

   ____

5. May I have the **recipe** for these delicious cookies? I want to learn how to make them.

   ____

6. Do you know her home **address**? I want to send her a letter.

   ____

7. The city was **ancient**. It must be at least a thousand years old.

   ____

8. Jane tried to **hurl** the ball high in the air, but it fell quickly to the ground .

   ____

At Home: Have students circle the context clues for each word.

Name________________________ Date______________ **Practice** 163

Main Idea

The **main idea** of a selection is the most important point, or what the information is about. **Supporting details** are "smaller" points that explain the main idea. Details may include examples, facts, or steps in a process.

Read the paragraphs below. After each, write the main idea and two supporting details.

The earth is made up of many layers. One layer contains oil, gas, and coal. The layer deep inside the earth is made of iron. It is very hot inside the center of the earth.

1. **Main Idea:** ________________________________

2. **Supporting Detail:** ________________________________

3. **Supporting Detail:** ________________________________

Although not all types of plants will grow in all places, you can grow many kinds of plants at home by planting a seed. First, fill a pot halfway to the top with soil. Place the seed in the soil and cover it with more soil. Then, water the soil. Some seeds, such as carrot seeds, grow very quickly.

4. **Main Idea:** ________________________________

5. **Supporting Detail:** ________________________________

6. **Supporting Detail:** ________________________________

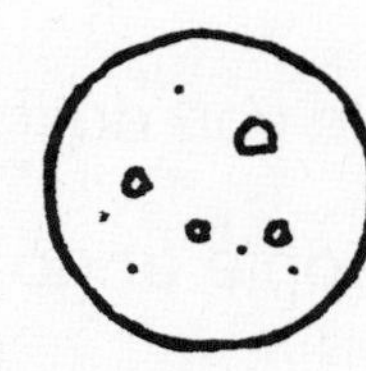

At Home: Have students look in an encyclopedia under "Earth" to find two more supporting details for the main idea: "The earth has many layers."

Vocabulary

Supply the correct words from the list to complete the sentence.

experiment	curious	scientific	discuss	advice	hero

For thousands of years, people had been ________________ about birds' ability to fly. It seemed like magic! By the early 1900s, there were true, ________________ explanations for the wonder of flight.

Orville and Wilbur Wright believed that they could create machines that would fly. The brothers did not write about or ________________ their ideas with many people. Instead, they followed their dreams, beginning with a simple ________________ that led to the world's first flight.

What would you do if you believed in something? Listen to ____________ from other people or go your own way? Sometimes the answers we find can change the lives of many people. Who knows? Someday you might be cheered as a ________________ for the discoveries you have made.

At Home: Have students use as many vocabulary words from this page as they can to write another passage.

A Book About Ben

Sam was *curious* about Ben Franklin. After school one day, he asked the librarian for a book about Franklin.

"Do you want to read about the *advice* he gave in his newspaper?" the librarian asked.

"No," said Sam.

"Do you want to know about Franklin forming the first public library?" the librarian asked.

"No," Sam replied.

"Do you want to know about Franklin's *scientific experiments*?"

"No," said Sam. "I want to find a book that will *discuss* what a great *hero* Franklin was."

The librarian smiled and led Sam to the perfect book.

1. How did Sam feel about Ben Franklin?

____

2. What did he first ask the librarian for?

____

3. What did Ben Franklin give in the newspaper?

____

4. What kind of *experiments* did Ben Franklin do?

____

5. What type of book did Sam want?

____

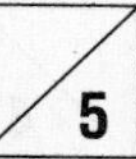

At Home: Have students name someone they would like to read about. Then have them write about why they think this person is important.

Name________________________________ Date______________ **Practice 165**

Story Comprehension

Complete the chart by listing details of some important things that Ben Franklin did during each time period.

Time Period	Details About Accomplishments
Franklin's early years in Boston.	
Franklin in Philadelphia from age 17 to age 42.	
Franklin in Philadelphia from age 42 until he left for England.	
Franklin in England, France, and America until his death at age 84.	

At Home: Have students write about the period of Franklin's life that is most interesting to them.

Follow Directions

Ben Franklin's early experiments in electricity paved the way for others. In 1825, Joseph Henry and William Sturgeon each created electromagnets.

You can make a simple one yourself. The directions below will show you how to do this. But they're all mixed up. There's a clue in every direction that will help you put them in the correct order. Number them correctly.

Note: If you'd like to try this experiment, ask an adult to help you.

_____ As a last step, hold the nail over the pins or clips. Then touch the second end of the wire to the other battery terminal.

_____ Gather these things to start: a 3-inch nail, 10 feet of insulated copper wire, a 6-volt battery, a few small paper clips, tacks, pins, or other small metal objects.

_____ The third thing to do is to put a piece of tape around the wound wire to keep it in place. The wire must be wound around the nail before you can do this step.

_____ After you've put the tape around the wire on the nail, strip the rubber insulation off the ends of both wires. Do not wind them around the nail.

_____ The second step is to begin to wind the wire around the nail. Leave about 1 foot of wire loose. Then wind the wire tightly from one end to the other. Leave another 1 foot of wire loose at the other end. Always wind in the same direction.

_____ The next-to-last step is to connect one end of the stripped wire to one end of the battery terminal.

Results: You'll see the nail become a magnet and lift up the pins. Take one wire off the battery and you'll see the pins drop back down. Electricity has made the nail into a magnet.

At Home: Have students write directions for a game they like to play.

Main Idea

When you read nonfiction, try to identify the **main ideas** and **supporting details** to help you understand what you are reading.

Look through "The Many Lives of Benjamin Franklin." List four supporting details for each main idea.

Main Idea: Benjamin Franklin was an inventor who made many discoveries.

Supporting Details

1. ______________________________

2. ______________________________

3. ______________________________

____

4. ______________________________

____

Main Idea: Franklin helped the American colonies win their independence from England and form a new government.

Supporting Details

5. ______________________________

____

6. ______________________________

7. ______________________________

8. ______________________________

At Home: Have students write the main idea and three supporting details for the story "The Many Lives of Benjamin Franklin."

Judgments and Decisions

Readers make **judgments** about story characters based on what they do and say.

Read the story and make a judgment about each character. Then list the reasons for your judgment.

The school play was to begin at 7 o'clock and Chang was trying to fix his costume. Then his little sister Ana ran into his room making an awful howling sound, and Chang stuck his finger with a pin.

"Ana! I'm busy. What's wrong?" he said, trying not to sound cross .

"No one will read to me. You read to me," she demanded. Chang said he was busy but that she could stay in his room if she would be quiet. Ana started howling again.

"OK, we'll play a game," Chang said. "If you help get my costume together, then I'll read."

Ana stopped crying and nodded yes.

Chang told her what he needed. Ana flew to the closet. Soon she had all the pieces of the costume piled neatly on Chang's bed.

1. Do you think that Chang was a good older brother? ____________

Reasons why:

2. ____

____

3. ____

4. What did you think of Ana before Chang said they would play a game?

____

Reason why:

5. ____

At Home: Ask students to write about a favorite story character and give some reasons why they like the character.

Root Words

Many of the words we use in English today are borrowed from two very old languages—Latin and Greek.

Each word below comes from the Latin word *scribere*, which means "to write." Complete each sentence using *script* or *scribble*. Then write the meaning of the word on the line below.

script scribble

1. I didn't have much time, so I had to ________________ him a note.

Meaning: ________________________________

2. Our teacher says that, after we learn how to print letters, she'll teach us how to write in ________________.

Meaning: ________________________________

Each word below comes from the Latin word *populus*, which means "people." Complete each sentence using *popular* or *public*. Then write the meaning of the word on the line below.

popular public

3. Anyone can use a ________________ beach.

Meaning: ________________________________

4. Everyone liked that book—it was very ________________

Meaning: ________________________________

At Home: Have students think of other words that have their roots in *scribere* or *populus*. Then have students tell what the words mean.

Name______________________ Date__________ **Practice** 170

Summarize

A **summary** is a brief statement that tells the main ideas or events of a selection.

Read the following story.

Toni's birthday was in one week. Toni gave the list of girls she wanted to invite to her party to her mother.

"Where is Sarah's name? Certainly you want to ask your best friend," her mother said as she went to fix dinner.

The truth was, Toni didn't feel like asking Sarah. Lately, Sarah was always walking home from school with May, a girl who had just started going to their school.

The day before the party, Sarah looked for Toni in the playground. "Happy birthday tomorrow," Sarah said.

"I hope we're still friends," Sarah continued. "You know, May would like to be your friend, too. She doesn't know very many people yet."

"She would? I thought you two were ignoring me," Toni said. "Well, why don't you both come over tomorrow?"

Later, Toni asked her mother if she could invite 11 people to her party.

"And maybe when I'm 11 I won't be so silly," she thought to herself.

Write a paragraph to summarize the main events in the story. Be sure to answer the following questions : What is Toni's problem? What does Sarah do? What does Toni do then?

____

____

____

____

____

At Home: Ask students to explain how they chose the information in their summary.

Name______________________ Date__________ **Practice 171**

Vocabulary

Write words from the box that mean almost the same thing as the underlined word or words.

avoid	brief	frequently	gradual	periods	report

1. I live in a place where it rains often. ______________
2. We heard an announcement on the radio that it would rain all day. ______________
3. Last year, there were several times when we had no rain at all. ______________
4. I keep away from the roads because I don't want to be splashed by cars. ______________
5. My brother did not take his umbrella because he saw a slow clearing in the sky. ______________
6. Sometimes the showers are short, but today it rained all day. ______________

The Weather Kids

It had rained every day for a week. Julia and Roy had to play inside. To *avoid* becoming bored, they pretended they were weather reporters.

First, Roy gave a *brief* weather *report*. He said that it would rain *frequently*.

Then Julia looked out the window and said, "There will be *periods* of rain with a *gradual* turning to snow."

Suddenly, Roy and Julia saw a rainbow and blue skies.

Roy gave one final report: "By the end of the day expect clearing skies." Julia laughed and the two headed outside. Finally they would be able to finish planting their spring garden.

1. What did Julia and Roy want to *avoid*?

____

2. What was Roy's weather *report* like?

____

3. In Roy's *report*, how often was it going to rain?

____

4. How was the change from rain to snow going to be?

____

5. Why did Roy say to expect clearing skies?

____

At Home: Encourage the students to talk about their favorite kinds of weather. What makes that kind of weather special or fun?

Name_______________________ Date__________ **Practice 172**

Story Comprehension

In "Cloudy With a Chance of Meatballs," Grandpa tells a bedtime story to the two children. Like most stories, Grandpa's tall tale about Chewandswallow involves a problem and a solution. The point where the main character or characters begin to solve the problem is the **turning point** of the story. Reread the story. Use what you read to fill in the chart.

	Plot Event	Explain
Problem	**1.** What is Chewandswallow's problem? ___________	
Problem	**2.** How does it get worse? ___________	
Solution	**3.** What is the turning point? ___________	
Solution	**4.** What action do people take to solve the problem? ___________	
Solution	**5.** Is the problem solved? ___________	

At Home: Ask students to tell about something that has changed in their life. Have them explain how things were before and how they are different now.

Name_______________________ Date_____________ **Practice 173**

Read Signs

Study the signs. Then read the statement about each sign. Is it **True** or **False**? Write your answer in the space on the right.

1. This sign is saying you can park all day on Monday. 

2. This sign warns you that traffic from two roads will come together into one road. 

3. This sign is telling you that the road will split in two up ahead. 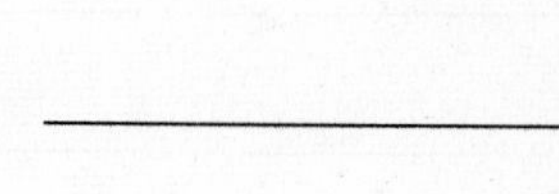

4. This sign is telling you that anyone can park here.

5. This sign is telling you where you can buy a kite for flying. 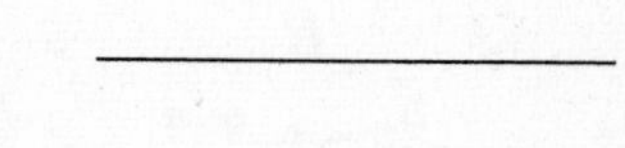

6. This sign is saying that you can't walk here.

At Home: Have students draw a traffic sign and tell what it means.

Name________________________ Date______________ **Practice 174**

Summarize

When you **summarize**, you tell the most important things that happened. A summary does not include small details.

Imagine that you are writing a report about "Cloudy With a Chance of Meatballs" for your school book fair. Write two paragraphs that summarize the story for your readers. Include only the most important parts of the story.

At Home: Ask students to tell you about the part of the story that they liked most.

Name____________________ Date__________ **Practice 175**

Judgments and Decisions

People use the information that they have to make **judgments** and to **decide** what to do.

Read the following passages. List the reasons for and against each decision and then tell what you would do.

Last night it snowed for the first time this winter. You want to go sleigh riding with your friends. Unfortunately, you have a sore throat. What should you do?

Reasons for going sleigh riding:

1. ____

____

Reason against going sleigh riding:

2. ____

3. What would you do? ______________________________

Imagine that your family just moved to a new town. Although you miss your friends from your old town, you are eager to make new friends. This coming weekend, you have been invited to two parties. One is with your old friends. The other is with people you have just met in your new town. You are having trouble deciding which party to attend.

Reason for going to the party with your old friends:

4. ____

Reason for going to the party with people in your new town:

5. ____

6. What would you do? ______________________________

At Home: Have students write about ways that they could stay friends with people from an old town and also make friends in a new town.

Name_________________________ Date___________ **Practice 176**

Root Words

Many English words come from Greek and Latin.

Each word below comes from the Latin word *cor,* which means "heart." Complete each sentence with the correct word.

discouraged encouraged courage

1. My teacher ___________________ me.

   She said that I was doing a good job.

2. After losing the race, I felt very sad and ___________________.

3. She is very brave. I would like to have as much __________ as she has.

Each word below comes from the Latin word *specere* which means "to look." Complete each sentence with the correct word.

spectacle respect expecting

4. Come in. I have been ___________________ you.

5. He is a great person. I ___________________ him.

6. Did you see the show? It was quite a ___________________.

At Home: Have students write definitions for the six words above.

Main Idea

The **main idea** is the most important point that an author wants readers to understand. **Supporting details** are the smaller examples and reasons that explain more about the main idea.

Read the following selection. List the supporting details that give more information about the main idea.

Amy Tan is a Chinese-American writer. Her parents were born in China, but she was born in California. Even when she was very young, people thought that she would become a good writer.

Amy Tan uses her own experiences to write her stories. Some of her stories tell what it is like to grow up in a Chinese family in America. In the book, *The Joy Luck Club*, she tells about a nine-year-old girl.

Amy Tan writes that the girl thinks her mother's Chinese customs are sometimes strange. Still, she listens to her mother's advice.

Main Idea: Amy Tan uses her own experience to write about being a Chinese American.

Supporting Details:

1. ____

2. ____

3. ____

____

4. ____

____

At Home: Have students write the main idea of a story they have recently read.

Name________________________ Date__________ **Practice 178**

Vocabulary

Answer **yes** or **no** to each question. Then explain your answer by writing a definition for the underlined word.

energy	pollution	future	entire	model	produce

1. Is electricity a kind of energy? ______________________________

____

2. If it took the entire family to push the car, does that mean that even the kids helped? ______________________________

____

3. Is there such thing as good pollution? ______________________________

____

4. Are flowers something that rose bushes produce? ______________________________

____

5. Is the past the same thing as the future? ______________________________

____

6. Is a real airplane a small copy of a model airplane? ______________________________

____

At Home: Have students use two or three of the vocabulary words in new sentences.

Teacher for the Future

David Edwards was planning his *future*. He drew a picture of what he would be when he grew up. Below the picture, he wrote, "I will be a *model* science teacher for the *entire* school."

David was concerned with natural resources and the environment. He hoped to teach people new ways to *produce energy*.

David also wanted to teach his students about *pollution*. He had several ideas for community clean-up projects. One project was to clean up all the trash near the stream downtown. Another project was to start a glass and plastic recycling center.

David's father was a farmer. From his father David had learned that it was important to take care of the world in which we live.

1. What did David want to be in the *future*?

2. How many students would David teach?

3. What did David hope to teach people to *produce*?

4. What else did David want to teach about?

5. How did David show he cared about the community?

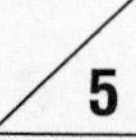

At Home: Invite students to draw posters showing ways people can make less pollution.

Name____________________ Date__________ **Practice 179**

Story Comprehension

Answer the following questions about "Pure Power!"

1. What is the main idea in "Pure Power!"? ____________________

2. Why are gas, coal, and oil called fossil fuels? ____________________

3. Where does solar power come from? ____________________

4. Where does a lot of the world's pollution come from? ____________________

5. How could sun power and wind power help keep the planet clean?

6. What is a solar farm? ____________________

7. Why might a family want to put tiles on the roof of their house to catch sunlight ? ____________________

8. Why have people built windmills? ____________________

At Home: Ask students to write what they learned about new forms of energy from reading "Pure Power!"

Name________________________ Date______________ **Practice 180**

Read an Ad

Compare the following advertisements. See how they use different ideas to interest you. Write **A** or **B** to answer each question.

A.

The Tree of Life Makes Your Life Easier

Eco Products introduces a New and Improved Plastic Bag Recycler. Dry your used plastic bags easily after they are cleaned. **Only $7.99**

Call: 1-800-555-5555 to order your Tree of Life

ECO PRODUCTS MAKE CENTS!

B.

1. Which ad is selling a product? ____________________

2. Which one is selling an idea? ____________________

3. Which ad is trying to get you to cooperate in a public service?

____

4. Which ad encourages you to buy something? ____________________

5. Which ad is brought to you by the Ad Group? ____________________

6. Which ad (or ads) suggests it has a way to save you money?

____

At Home: Have students make up their own ad for an ecological product.

Name______________________ Date___________ **Practice 181**

Fact and Nonfact

Decide whether each statement is a **fact** or an **opinion**. For facts, explain how to prove them to be true—for example, by using a book or an encyclopedia, by asking an expert, or by seeing something firsthand.

1. People need to find new forms of energy because we will run out of coal and oil in the future. ______________________

____

2. In Japan some houses have roofs built with tiles that collect sunlight.

____

____

3. New kinds of windmills can catch more wind than the old ones.

____

4. Eggs taste better when they are cooked by sun power. __________

____

5. Fossil fuels are formed from the fossils of plants and animals that lived millions of years ago. ______________________

____

6. Someday, cars may run on energy made from the sun. __________

____

At Home: Have students give an example of a fact and an opinion about energy.

Root Words

Knowing the **etymology**, or history, of a word can help you figure out the meaning.

Read about the **root words** below. Then write the meaning for the word in dark type. If you are having trouble, look the word up in a dictionary.

1. **Perfect** comes from the Latin *per*, "completely," and *facere*, "to make."

   ____

2. **Contact** comes from the Latin *con*, "together," and *tangere*, "touch."

   ____

3. **Auditorium** comes from the Latin *audire*, "to hear," and *orium*, "a place for."

   ____

   ____

4. **Disappear** comes from the Latin *dis*, "to do away with something that has been done," and *apparere*, "come into view."

   ____

5. **Excite** comes from the Latin *ex*, "out," and *ciere*, "to call."

   ____

6. **Introduce** comes from the Latin *intro*, "to the inside," and *ducere*, "to lead."

   ____

At Home: Have students try to write one sentence that includes three of the words above.

Context Clues

To figure out the meaning of an unfamiliar word, try reading the words around it.

Match the word in dark type in each sentence in the left-hand column with its definition in the right-hand column. Write the letter of the definition on the line.

_____ **1.** Yesterday, we had no school because of the **storm**. It snowed all day long.

_____ **2.** That shirt is too **expensive**. I want one that doesn't cost so much.

_____ **3.** The children were very **noisy**. Their father said, "Quiet down, kids. You're being too loud!"

_____ **4.** I saw a huge black **crow** flying outside. It was the biggest bird I had ever seen.

_____ **5.** We grow flowers in our **garden**, but some people grow vegetables instead.

_____ **6.** In the **future**, there will be more bicycles, just you wait and see!

a. a large bird with black feathers

b. a strong wind with snow or rain

c. having a high price

d. time to come

e. loud

f. a piece of ground where flowers or vegetables are grown

At Home: Have students underline the context clues in each sentence.

Name________________________ Date____________ **Practice 184**

Unit 2 Vocabulary Review

A. If the underlined word means almost the same as the vocabulary word, write **S** on the line. If it means the opposite, write **O**.

1. **entire** — Lu Yee read the whole book in a week. _____
2. **frequently** — Roy often stays with his grandmother. _____
3. **brief** — Wanda took a long rest. _____
4. **delighted** — Jenny was glad to see her friend. _____
5. **rapidly** — Ellen walked home slowly. _____
6. **curious** — The nosy child peeked in the closet. _____

B. Read each question. Then choose a word from the box to answer each question. Write your answer on the line.

hero	pollution	route	temperature

1. If people throw garbage in the river, what will they cause?

____

2. If you did a brave thing, what would you be?

____

3. If you check how hot it is outside, what would you measure?

____

4. If you followed certain streets to get to school, what would you have?

____

At Home: Have students write a story about an adventure they had. Encourage them to use at least three vocabulary words in their story.

Unit 2 Vocabulary Review

A. Supply the correct vocabulary word.

future	model	label	furious	discuss

1. The ________________ on the shirt tells what size it is.

2. We always ________________ the stories we read at school.

3. When Carl's little sister broke his kite, he was ________________.

4. Alice likes to build ________________ boats.

5. Since this is winter, summer is in the ________________.

B. Answer the questions. Then explain your answer by telling what the word means.

1. Which is scientific, to guess what will happen or to figure it out?

____

2. If companies produce stuffed animals, do they make or sell them?

____

3. Could an animal with claws scratch or bite you? ________________

____

4. When something is gradual, is it fast or slow? ________________

____

5. If things are disguised, are they hidden or recognized? ________________

____

At Home: Have students write questions for the vocabulary words in Part A. They can use the questions in Part B as a guide.

Name_________________________ Date_____________ **Practice 186**

Make Inferences

Sometimes an author tells you plainly what is happening in a story. At other times, readers must **infer**, or figure out, what is happening. Readers look for clues the author gives that **show** what is happening.

Read the following passages. Look for clues in each passage to help answer the questions.

Grandpa John cleaned and polished his old car until it shone like a new penny. He spent all morning on it, and in the afternoon he planned to work on the motor.

1. How does Grandpa feel about his car? _______________

____

2. Explain how you know. _______________

____

The white peaks got higher and higher. They could change shape in a second—now they were rolling, snowy mountains. Alex took a taste. He put in more sugar and cream. Then he whipped up some clouds in the big blue bowl.

3. What is Alex doing ? _______________

____

4. Explain how you know. _______________

____

____

5. How does the author show that Alex has a good imagination?

____

____

At Home: Have students explain what it means to make inferences.

Vocabulary

Write words from the list to complete the story.

accept	equipment	invisible	mistakes	perform	talented

We have a cooking club at our school. On Friday, Ms. Parker showed us how to bake bread. She is a ____________ baker who knows how to make all kinds of breads, cakes, and pies. We were lucky to be able to see her ________________.

First she gathered her bowls, pans, and other __________. Then she mixed yeast and warm water. "Don't make any ______________ here," she said. "If the water is too hot, the yeast won't work."

Ms. Parker mixed the yeast with flour to make dough. "You can't see the yeast now," she said. "But even though it's ______________, it's hard at work making the dough rise." She was right. Soon that dough was twice as big as before. And the bread Ms. Parker baked from it was delicious.

So come join our cooking club! We are always happy to ________ new members. You will learn a lot and have fun, too.

At Home: Have students make up one question about the story that could be answered **Yes** and one question that could be answered **No**.

No Mistake About It

Joy loved baseball, but she did not feel *talented* enough to play. She also felt too shy to *perform* in front of fans.

Sometimes Joy carried *equipment* onto the field for the Aces, her older sister's team. Joy carried the bats, gloves, and balls. But once on the field, she felt *invisible*. It was as though no one saw her.

Joy wished that the Aces would *accept* her as a member of the team. Joy really wanted to be more than a team helper.

One Saturday, Joy's wish came true. Her sister had a cold and couldn't play in the game. Joy took her place. And without making any *mistakes*, she led the Aces to win the game!

1. What are some kinds of *equipment* used in baseball?

___

2. How did Joy feel once she got on the field and no one saw her?

___

3. What did Joy wish the Aces would do?

___

4. What did Joy do without any mistakes?

___

5. How do you think Joy *performed* in the game?

___

At Home: Encourage students to talk about a time they felt shy. Why did they feel that way? What helped them feel less shy?

Name_______________________ Date___________ Practice 188

Story Comprehension

Think about "The Bat Boy and His Violin." Then complete the chart below.

1. Setting of story	______________________
2. Main characters	______________________
3. Beginning of story	______________________
4. Middle of story	______________________
5. End of story	______________________

 At Home: Have students illustrate a baseball field.

Name________________________________ Date______________ **Practice 189**

Use the Library

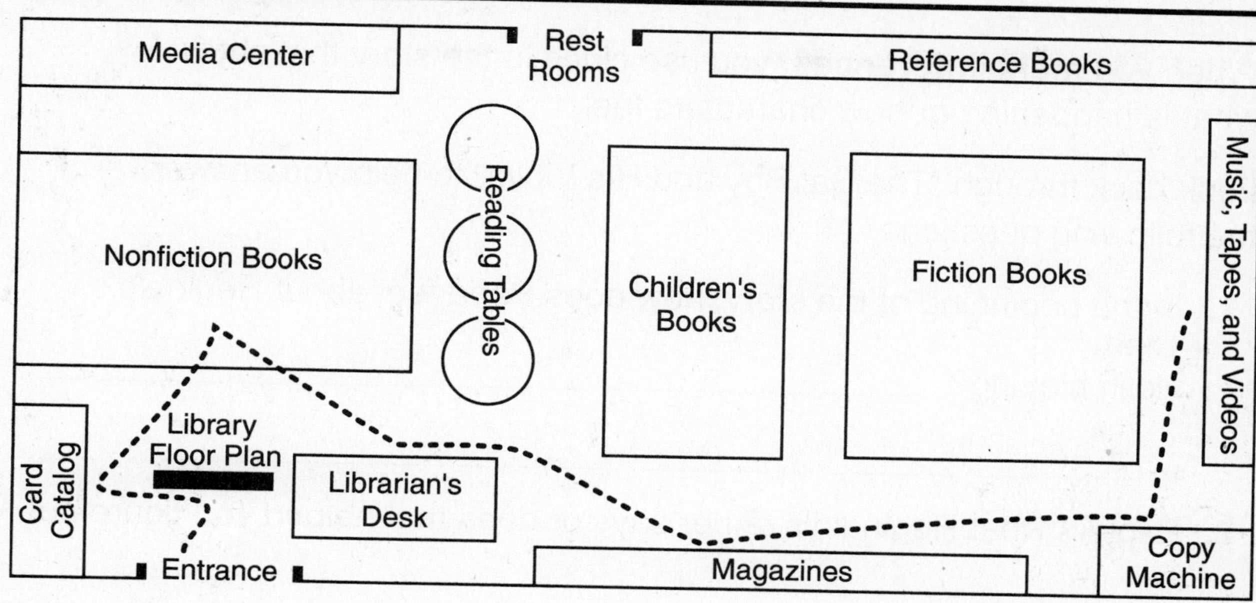

Write down the area of the library visited by the student to complete her task.

1. I look up *piano* and see 786.2 B for the book *Pianos*, by Hal Barber.

   ____

2. I find the 700s on the shelves of books. The book is checked out.

   ____

3. I go to the librarian. She suggests a magazine called *Modern Piano*.

   ____

4. In this magazine I find a great article about a piano factory.

   ____

5. I decide to make a copy to take home for my report.

   ____

6. I pick up a tape of great piano music to hear modern pianos.

   ____

At Home: Ask students to tell where they go first when they visit the library.

Name_______________ Date_______________ **Practice 190**

Make Inferences

When you **make inferences**, you use clues in the story that show what is happening or how characters feel.

Look back through "The Bat Boy and His Violin" to help you answer the following questions.

1. In the beginning of the story, how does Papa feel about Reginald's violin playing? _______________

____

2. Explain what Reginald's father says or does that helped you figure out your answer. _______________

____

____

____

3. At the beginning of the story, does Papa think that Reginald is a good bat boy? Explain your answer. _______________

____

____

4. Is Papa surprised when they can't find a hotel that will let the baseball team stay overnight? Explain your answer. _______________

____

____

5. At the end of the story, why is Reginald afraid that his father won't like his music anymore? _______________

At Home: Ask students to explain how Papa's feelings about Reginald's playing the violin change during the story.

Name______________________ Date____________ **Practice 191**

Author's Purpose, Point of View

An author's main **purpose** in writing may be to inform, to entertain, or to persuade. Read each passage. Write the author's main purpose. Then evaluate the author's **point of view**.

You should go to the circus. I went last night. It was so exciting! First, a clown shot out of the dark, jumped on a horse's back, and did tricks. Then he chose a boy from the audience and gave him a scarf. Next the clown tugged at the scarf and a bird flew out of it. The Big Clown Circus will be at City Center for two weeks. I plan to go again!

1. What is the author's main purpose? Explain. ______________________

____

2. What do you think is the author's point of view about the circus? Why?

____

____

This is how to make a very tasty fruit salad. Use fruits that you like, such as apples, berries, bananas, or watermelon. Wash all the fruit and cut it up into small pieces. Put the cut-up fruit into a bowl. Make sure you don't get any seeds in the bowl. Then cut an orange in half. Squeeze each half of the orange over the fruit and stir.

3. What is the author's main purpose? Explain. ______________________

____

4. Does the author seem to think that it is worth the trouble to make fruit salad? What in the passage makes you answer as you did? __________

____

At Home: Ask students to find a story or article that was written for the purpose of entertaining an audience.

Multiple-Meaning Words

Multiple-meaning words have more than one meaning. The words and sentences around a word are **context clues**.

Use context clues in each sentence to find the meaning of the underlined word. Circle the letter of the best meaning. Then write a sentence for each multiple-meaning word using a **different** meaning of the word.

1. They cut through the field instead of walking around it.

   a. to divide with something sharp **b.** to cross or pass

   ____

2. It's hot in here—let's turn on the fan.

   a. something that is used to move the air **b.** a person who is very enthusiastic about something

   ____

3. I'm learning how to fence. It's a hard sport.

   a. something that is used to mark off an area **b.** the sport of fighting with a sword

   ____

4. The fly buzzed around my head.

   a. an insect with two wings **b.** to move through the air

   ____

5. The audience cheered and gave the singer a big hand.

   a. the end part of the arm **b.** clapping

   ____

At Home: Have students underline the context clue that helped them to define the underlined word in each sentence.

Name ______________________ Date ____________ **Practice 193**

Draw Conclusions

You can **draw conclusions** about story characters and events by paying attention to facts you find in the selection.

Read the selection. Then answer each question to draw a conclusion.

Max lost his backpack. He looked on the floor, but all he saw were people's feet and the wheels of the shopping carts.

If my backpack is lost, so is my science report and my lucky baseball, Max thought.

Max searched for a lumpy, green backpack. Finally, he thought, Mom is going to buy a birthday cake. I better go tell her what happened.

Max let his nose lead him toward the bakery section. As the smell of pies and cookies became stronger, he saw her.

"Whew," he said to her. "It sure smells good around here." Then he spied something buried under all his mother's groceries. It was lumpy and green.

1. How do you think Max feels when he finds out he doesn't have his backpack? ______________________________
____

2. What are some of Max's activities? ______________________
____

3. Why does Max go to find his mother in the bakery section? ________
____

4. What does Max spy in his mother's shopping cart? ____________
____

At Home: Ask students to draw some conclusions about what Max and his mother will do next.

Vocabulary

Identify the context clues in each sentence that could help you figure out the meaning of each underlined word.

1. I couldn't eat the sauce because it had a sharp, bitter taste. ____________

____

2. Each crystal of sugar is as big as a tiny piece of salt or a grain of sand.

____

3. The boy gripped the handrail tightly as he slowly climbed the steep staircase. ____________

4. In Africa's animal kingdom, lions rule over many other animals of the region. ____________

5. One minute the bird was on the windowsill, and the next minute it was gone; it had simply vanished. ____________

____

6. My head was dizzy from the whirling motion of the fairground ride.

____

At Home: Have students define each of the vocabulary words above in their own words.

The Hungry Dream

One night Jeremy dreamed of a faraway *kingdom*. The sky was yellow. The *whirling* red clouds were like spinning wheels. The grass was so tall, Jeremy *vanished* when he walked in it.

In the dream, Jeremy felt hungry. But he didn't see any food. He did see a path that led to a large shiny shape. When he got closer, he saw that it was a giant *crystal* with many points and sides. It had a door just big enough for Jeremy to enter.

Inside, people were eating. Jeremy ate the food, but it had a *bitter* taste. While he ate, the ground began to shake. Jeremy *gripped* the table.

Suddenly ... Jeremy woke up. The sky outside his window was blue!

1. Why was it that Jeremy *vanished* while walking in the far away *kingdom*?

____

2. What were the clouds in this *kingdom* doing?

____

3. How did the food Jeremy ate taste?

____

4. What is another way to say "held tightly" in this story?

____

5. Why does this *kingdom* appear and then disappear?

____

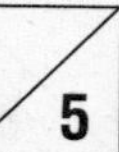

At Home: Have students draw and color an imaginary kingdom.

Name ______________________ Date ____________ **Practice 195**

Story Comprehension

Review "Two Bad Ants." Then, in a few words or a sentence, describe the different parts of the story listed below.

1. First setting of story: ____________________

2. Second setting of story: ____________________

3. Main characters: ____________________

4. Point of view: ____________________

5. Beginning of story: ____________________

____

____

6. Middle of story: ____________________

____

____

____

7. End of story: ____________________

____

____

8. Message of story: ____________________

____

____

At Home: Ask students to list the ways the ants described household items. Then ask them why the author didn't call these items by their familiar names.

Do an Author and Title Search

A card catalog can help you find a book by its title or by the author's name.

To use a card catalog on a computer, you need to type in a Keyword. This can be either the author's last name, a word from the title, or the subject. Try to choose a word that probably won't appear in a lot of other titles.

Read the problem stated below. Decide if it would be better to do an author or a title search. Write **Author** or **Title** in the space beside the problem. Then choose a Keyword you might use to find the book you want.

	Author or Title	Keyword
1. You read a book by Dr. Seuss. Now you'd like to find other books he's written.	________	________________
2. You read a book last year with the word *elephants* in the title. But you don't remember the whole name.	________	________________
3. You want to find out who wrote "The Wind in the Willows."	________	________
4. Margaret Wise Brown is your favorite author. You want to see if she wrote any books of poetry.	________	________
5. You're looking for a book about Greek myths written by Rosemary Wells.	________	________________

At Home: Have students list two books they found by searching a library card catalog.

Draw Conclusions

A **conclusion** is what you decide to think about something after you have looked at the information. You can draw a conclusion about a story by considering the information the author gives you. You also can use what you know from your own experiences.

Draw your own conclusions about the two ants by answering each question.

1. Do you think the ants enjoyed their day in the kitchen? __________

2. What information from the story helped you to draw your conclusion?

____

____

3. Think about a challenging day you have had or a time when you had some unexpected surprises. How did you feel afterward? __________

____

4. How do you think the ants felt after they returned home? __________

____

5. What information did you use to draw that conclusion? Think about information from the story and what you know from experience.

____

____

____

6. Do you think the two ants will ever stay behind again? Why or why not?

____

____

At Home: Have students choose an event from the story, such as when the ants were in the cup of coffee and draw a conclusion about how the ants felt and why.

Author's Purpose, Point of View

Authors often have a **point of view,** or opinion about something, which they express through their writing.

Read the following passage. Then answer the questions about the author's purpose and point of view.

I hadn't been back to my hometown of Lakeside for thirty years. I expected to find some changes, but nothing had changed. I found out that an ice-cream cone still cost 25 cents. A sign at the Center Movie House said, "Come early to see the latest cartoon before the movie." And guess what? The movie cost 75 cents. But it wasn't the low prices that bothered me. It was the ghostly quiet and the deserted streets. I wondered what had happened.

1. Tell some things about the story that entertained you.

____

____

2. What did the story inform you about the past?

____

____

3. What is the author trying to persuade you to believe? ____________

____

4. What do you think is the author's attitude about Lakeside?

____

____

5. What do you think is the author's main purpose for writing the story?

____

At Home: Ask students to explain their answer to question 5.

Context Clues

To figure out the meaning of a new word, look at the words and sentences around it for clues.

Read each sentence and look at the underlined word. Circle the words or phrases that help you figure out the meaning of the underlined word. Then write the meaning on the line.

1. I hurt one of the fingers on my hand, so it was hard for me to write.

____

2. I knew her name, but then I forgot it. I wish I could remember it.

____

3. To make gray paint, mix black paint with white paint.

____

4. The chair was too hard for me, so I sat in a softer one.

____

5. I heard a cat meowing softly.

____

6. May is my favorite month of the year. My mother's favorite month is March.

____

7. My shadow on the wall is much larger than I am. The light from the lamp made everything look different.

____

8. He lost his burro in the thick jungle. The little gray animal could not be found.

____

At Home: Challenge students to write two sentences that include all of the underlined words above.

Make Inferences

Sometimes characters don't say exactly how they feel or what they are thinking. So readers must **infer** what the characters feel by what they say or how they act.

Read the descriptions in the left-hand column. Then, in the right-hand column, tell how you think each character feels.

What the Character Says, Thinks, or Does	How the Character Feels
Before she went to bed, Ann made sure the kitten had food and water. She put out an extra bowl of water, just in case. Ann put down three more blankets in the box the kitten slept in.	**1.** Ann ______________
"I have never seen such a beautiful birthday cake," Grandfather said. "I can't believe you went to so much trouble just for me."	**2.** Grandfather ______________
Jason and Steve both wanted to be Captain Hook in the school play. Jason got the part. Steve tried hard to put on a happy face before he met Jason after school.	**3.** Steve ______________
Rolf brought his two mice to class. When she saw the mice, Claire gripped the edge of her desk. She hoped she wouldn't burst into tears in front of the whole class.	**4.** Claire ______________

At Home: Have students show you the clues in the descriptions that helped them make their inferences.

Name____________________ Date__________ **Practice 201**

Vocabulary

solve	crafty	communicate	brain	social	subject

1. Most apes are very ________________ and like to live together in large groups.
2. Some people ________________ with each other by using sign language.
3. Scientists don't know much about what goes on inside the ________________ of an animal.
4. Animal behavior is one ________________ that scientists like to study.
5. Mice are clever and can be ________________ when it comes to hiding and gathering food.
6. Many animals can ________________ simple problems such as where to find food.

At Home: Ask students to make up one sentence that uses three of the vocabulary words on this page.

Jake the Brain

Jake is my cat. He is the smartest cat in the world. He is so smart that he can *solve* math problems. You might wonder how he learned about this *subject*. After all, Jake doesn't go to school. You might also wonder how Jake can *communicate* his answer.

First, you should know that Jake is a very *social* cat. He likes to work with people. Also, when it comes to math, Jake really uses his *brain*.

Sometimes I show Jake a piece of cat food. Next, I show him two more pieces. Then I ask him how many pieces there are. Jake puts his paw on one piece and meows. Then he puts his paw on the other two pieces and meows twice. I count the meows for the answer: three pieces of food! That is some *crafty* cat!

1. What school *subject* does Jake the cat know?

____

2. What word in this story means "to pass along information"?

____

3. What word describes the cat when he likes to work with others?

____

4. What can Jake do with math problems?

____

5. How does Jake's owner feel about him?

____

At Home: Have students make a crossword puzzle using the italicized words from the story.

Name ______________________ Date ______________ **Practice 202**

Story Comprehension

Think about "Do Animals Think?" Then complete the charts below.

Examples of Animals' Thinking	Animals' Instincts
1.	6.
2.	7.
3.	8.
4.	9.
5.	10.
	11.
	12.

At Home: Ask students to explain why a sea otter using a stone as a hammer to open a shell is different from a chimp choosing the best tool to crack a nut.

Name_______________________________ Date____________ **Practice 203**

Use an Encyclopedia Index

Below you will see a sample page from an encyclopedia index. Use it to answers the questions that follow.

636 **Money**

Money M:649 *with pictures*
Coins: Ci:439 *with pictures*
Gold: G:234
Shells (as money): S:324
Mongolia M:652 *with map*
Monkey (animal) **M:659** *with pictures and map*
Spider S:543 *with picture*
Monster (legends)
Dragon D:789
Loch Ness L:238 *with picture*
See also **Myths**
Montana M:713 *with pictures and maps*

1. What is the last entry word on this page? ____________________

2. What is the guide word for this page? ____________________

3. In what volume and on what page would you find information on the state of Montana? ____________________

4. In what volume and on what page would you find a picture of a spider monkey? ____________________

5. In what volume and on what page would you find a map of Mongolia?

____

At Home: Ask students where they would look for a map of Montana.

Make Inferences

When you read a nonfiction story, you can use the story's details to help you make **inferences**. The details can suggest the author's purpose for writing or the author's point of view about the subject.

Think about "Do Animals Think?" Read each question below. Write your inference. Then list one or two details in the story that help you explain your inference.

1. What are the author's feelings about animals?

   Inference: ______________________________

   Details: ______________________________

   ____

   ____

2. Does the author think that scientists know everything about how animals "think"?

   Inference: ______________________________

   ____

   Details: ______________________________

   ____

   ____

3. Does the author think that only human beings are smart?

   Inference: ______________________________

   Details: ______________________________

   ____

   ____

At Home: Ask students to infer if a sheep is thinking when it tries not to leave the flock after a sheepdog has singled it out.

Name________________________ Date____________ **Practice 205**

Form Generalizations

Some **generalizations** are comments, observations, or opinions that are based on a character's feelings or actions in a story.

Use the passage to answer the questions.

Carlos was telling his cousins about the time Aunt Marie went to work on a farm in California and ended up as an extra in a movie. Carlos loved telling the stories he had heard so often from his father. He thought they were exciting.

"Who cares," Susan stopped him. "Let's go out and play baseball."

That evening at dinner Carlos's father and uncle talked about their grandfather and how he first came to Texas from Mexico. When they spoke in Spanish, his cousins didn't even bother to listen. Carlos knew that none of the cousins spoke Spanish as well as their parents did, himself included. Still, he thought it was kind of cool to know two languages.

1. How do people feel when others ignore them? ____________

____

2. What can you learn by listening to older people? ____________

____

3. What does the story suggest about the difference between younger people and older people? ____________

____

4. Why do you think that Carlos and his cousins don't speak Spanish as well as their parents do? ____________

____

____

At Home: Ask students to form a generalization about what people can learn by listening to family stories.

Name____________________ Date__________ **Practice 206**

Multiple-Meaning Words

Words with more than one meaning are called **multiple-meaning words**. The words and sentences around a multiple-meaning word can help you define the word.

Read each sentence below. Use **context clues** in each sentence to define the meaning of each underlined word. Then match each multiple-meaning word with its definition. Write the letter of the definition on the line.

____ **1.** It took us a <u>long</u> time to get home.	**a.**	angry
____ **2.** That hat is <u>mine</u>, not yours.	**b.**	a tool to cut wood
____ **3.** She was <u>cross</u> with me because I took her pencil without asking.	**c.**	belonging to me
____ **4.** I <u>saw</u> her new toy.	**d.**	have in mind
____ **5.** It was <u>mean</u> of you to make fun of him.	**e.**	move from one side to the other
____ **6.** The men worked in the coal <u>mine</u>.	**f.**	to want very much
____ **7.** I <u>long</u> to visit my grandmother in Florida.	**g.**	not nice
____ **8.** You don't understand what I <u>mean</u>.	**h.**	not short
____ **9.** I want a <u>saw</u> for my birthday.	**i.**	looked at
____ **10.** She let me <u>cross</u> the street	**j.**	a large space under the ground

At Home: Have students check their answers in a dictionary.

/10

Draw Conclusions

When you **draw conclusions**, you look for facts in the story to help you answer a question.

Read each set of facts and then read the conclusions. Which conclusion can you draw based on the facts? Write an **X** next to the correct conclusion.

FACTS	CONCLUSIONS
1. It takes 3 hours to wash two cars. Mary and Jo can work for 4 hours.	_____ Mary and Jo can wash two cars. _____ Mary and Jo can only wash one car.
2. The rain filled the swimming pool all the way up to the top. Mr. Cray kept one eye on the clouds and one eye on the plug.	_____ Mr. Cray may pull the plug if it keeps on raining. _____ Mr. Cray counted on the rain to fill the pool.
3. Ray promised to clean up his room after dinner. First though, he planned to watch a show about lions on TV.	_____ Ray enjoys cleaning his room. _____ Ray may clean up his room after he watches a show.
4. The truck shook and shook. Tina was afraid that the oranges were about to roll off onto the bumpy dirt road.	_____ Tina is driving on a bumpy dirt road. _____ Tina's truck is broken.
5. Anna's eyes filled with tears as she went up to accept her award and thank the audience.	_____ Anna is upset. _____ Anna is very happy.

At Home: Ask students to tell you about a time when they drew the wrong conclusion about a situation.

Name__________________________ Date______________ **Practice 208**

Vocabulary

Supply the vocabulary word that has almost the same meaning as the underlined words in each sentence.

considering conversation boasting hesitated interrupted seized

1. Dad paused for a moment before diving into the pool.

   ____

2. The mouse grabbed the piece of cheese. ____________________

3. Julie always broke in while her mother was speaking.

   ____

4. René was bragging about the size of his boat. ________________

5. Keeping in mind that she hadn't rehearsed, Sarah played her part well.

   ____

6. My brother and I had a

   friendly talk.

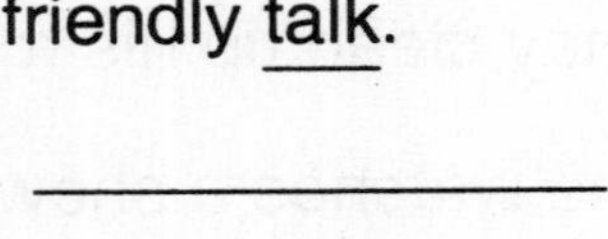

At Home: Have students make up three sentences, each using two of the vocabulary words.

The Buzz About Flies

When the teacher asked Andrew to work with Cicely on a science project, both students looked unhappy. They had never even had a *conversation* before. They didn't know each other.

Cicely *hesitated* to tell Andrew about her project idea. When she began to speak about it, she was *interrupted* by a loud buzz.

Andrew reached up and *seized* a fly. As he was *boasting* about how he had caught the fly, it flew out of his hand.

"I'll get it," Cicely said. She followed the fly quietly.

When it landed on a wall, she cupped her hand around it. "I've got it!" she said. "And I've got an idea for our project!"

Considering what had just happened, Andrew was not surprised to hear Cicely's idea. "We should do our project on flies," she suggested.

1. What had Andrew and Cicely never had with each other?

____

2. What was it that Cicely *hesitated* to do?

____

3. How was Cicely *interrupted*?

____

4. What did Andrew do when the fly was buzzing?

____

5. How did the fly end up being helpful to Cicely and Andrew?

____

At Home: Encourage students to make a small science project by drawing and labeling an insect or animal they would like to know more about.

Story Comprehension

Think about "Wilbur's Boast." Then write a sentence or sentences to fill in the chart.

1. SETTING:

____

2. HOW DOES THE SETTING AFFECT THE PLOT?

____

____

3. MAIN CHARACTERS:

____

____

4. DESCRIBE EACH MAIN CHARACTER:

____

____

____

5. PLOT:

____

At Home: Have students draw a picture to accompany one of their answers.

Name________________________ Date____________ **Practice 210**

Do an Electronic Subject Search

An electronic subject search on a library computer will tell you what books will give you information. Pretend you typed in the subject "Farming Today." Here is what the computer's first screen shows.

```
Farming Today
```

```
1. Life on a Farm             Nicole Erwin    ©1998  Click Here for Full Record
2. Farm Equipment Repairs     Bruce Quilby    ©1995  Click Here for Full Record
3. Backwoods Vermont          Tanya Pullan    ©1994  Click Here for Full Record
4. The Last Family Farm       Barry Langlen   ©1988  Click Here for Full Record

38 books found       (B) = go back       (R) = go to next screen
```

Answer the following questions by using the results of the computer catalog search.

1. Which book was published most recently? ____________

2. Which book would tell you how to repair a tractor? ____________

3. How many different books did the computer find? ____________

4. Which book contains information about just one state? ____________

5. How would you see more of this list? ____________

At Home: Ask students to list three subjects they would like to investigate in a subject search by computer.

Name____________________ Date__________

Draw Conclusions

Readers can **draw conclusions** about a character or a story event based on the information and facts they find in the story.

Answer each question by using information in "Wilbur's Boast" to draw a conclusion.

1. Why does Wilbur look around to see if a piece of rope was following him the first time he falls? ____________________

2. How does Charlotte feel when Wilbur falls the first time? ____________________

3. Why does Wilbur climb to the top of the pile and try to spin a web again?

4. How do Charlotte and Fern feel about Wilbur?

5. How does Wilbur feel about falling when he tried to spin a web?

6. Why does Charlotte tell the story about the bridge?

At Home: Ask your students to draw conclusions about who is older and wiser, Charlotte or Wilbur.

Name____________________ Date__________ **Practice 212**

Form Generalizations

Read each generalization about fairy tales. Tell whether you think the generalization is true or false. Then explain your answer. You may want to use the name of a fairy tale as an example.

1. Fairy tales are make-believe.

____

2. Some fairy tales have characters who are mean people.

____

3. Fairy tales are too scary for little children to hear or watch.

____

4. Many fairy tales begin by saying, "Once upon a time..."

____

5. Everyone loves fairy tales. ________________________

Context Clues

If you see an unfamiliar word, try looking at the words and phrases around it for **context clues**.

Read each sentence and look at the underlined word. Write the correct meaning for the word. Then write a new sentence that includes the underlined word.

1. My mother has a different last name than I do. Her last name is Moser, and my last name is Brown.

   Meaning: ________________

   Sentence: ________________

2. Today, we discussed pollution. People talked a lot about it.

   Meaning: ________________

   Sentence: ________________

3. I saw some men fishing down by the lake. The fishermen asked me if I wanted to learn how to fish.

   Meaning: ________________

   Sentence: ________________

4. If you throw a ball in water, it will not sink. It will float on top.

   Meaning: ________________

   Sentence: ________________

At Home: Have students circle the context clues in the examples.

Author's Purpose, Point of View

Authors write for different **purposes**. They may write to inform, to entertain, or to persuade. For example, the purpose of a report may be to inform; the purpose of a fiction story may be to entertain; and the purpose of a letter or an advertisement may be to persuade.

Think of a subject to write about for each purpose listed below. Then write a sentence about each subject.

Inform

1. Subject:

   ____

2. About subject:

   ____

   ____

Entertain

3. Subject:

   ____

4. About subject:

   ____

   ____

Persuade

5. Subject:

   ____

6. About subject:

   ____

   ____

At Home: Encourage students to include a small drawing with each of their subject choices.

Name______________________________ Date______________ **Practice 215**

Vocabulary

Fill in the blanks with the correct word. Both blank lines for each number should be filled in with the same word.

rescuers	loops	snug	starve	strip	crates

1. We packed the oranges in large ______________ to ship them overseas. ______________ keep things in place while they travel over a long distance.

2. The bear cubs were warm and ______________ in their cave throughout the winter. We were safe and ______________ in our house!

3. The trainer gently ______________ the rope around the horse's neck. Then she ______________ the other end of the rope around a fence post and ties it tightly.

4. Thanks to the ______________ we were all saved from the freezing cold. It took the ______________ four hours to find us.

5. During the winter, many animals ______________ bark from the trees for food. They ______________ moss from rocks and eat that as well.

6. Bears eat plenty of food during the fall, so they don't ______________ during the cold and snowy winter. We store lots of food in the kitchen, so we don't ______________ either!

At Home: Have students choose one of the vocabulary words and make up two related sentences, each of which includes the word.

A Trip to Remember

One day while camping, I heard a noise in the woods. My family walked toward the noise. We found a baby bear with its leg caught in the *loops* of a rope.

The rope was tied around a tree. When the bear pulled at the rope, it would *strip* off the bark of the tree.

My mother and I waited near the baby bear while my father went to the park ranger's cabin. This bear needed some trained *rescuers*.

When the ranger came she had two *crates*: a large one and a small one. The bear fit in the small one. Now it was safe and *snug*.

"I will feed the bear right away so it will not *starve*," said the ranger. "Then we'll find the bear's home."

That was one camping trip I will always remember!

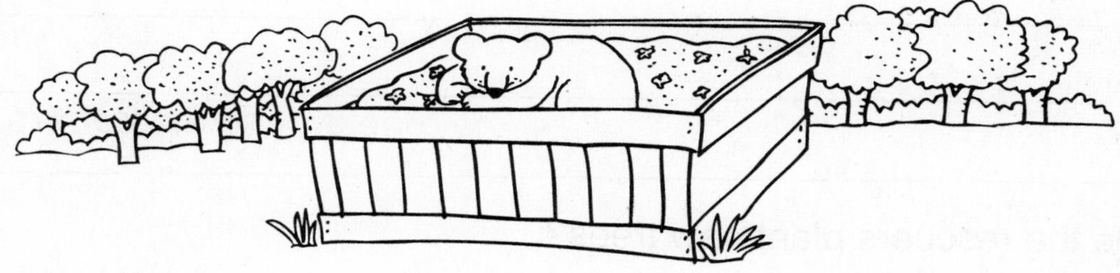

1. What was the bear caught in?

____

2. What did the bear *strip* off the tree?

____

3. Who did the father go to look for at the park ranger's cabin?

____

4. What made the baby bear safe and *snug*?

____

5. Why does the speaker say that was a trip always to be remembered?

____

At Home: Invite students to write a short story about rescuing an animal in danger.

Story Comprehension

Suppose you are writing a summary of "The Koala Catchers." Review the information in the selection. Then write answers to the following questions.

Where does the story take place?

1. ____________________

When does the story take place?

2. ____________________

What do the rescuers do?

3. ____________________

____

4. ____________________

____

Why do the rescuers plant new trees?

5. ____________________

____

6. ____________________

____

What are koalas like?

7. ____________________

____

8. ____________________

____

At Home: Ask students to tell you how the fact that koalas only eat eucalyptus leaves causes problems for them.

Name______________________ Date____________ **Practice 217**

Use a Resource

When you're doing a student project, you might choose to use one or more of these resources for information.

newspaper encyclopedia dictionary

card catalog telephone book

Which resources would you use to complete each project below? Write their names and the information you could find in each one.

1. You want to find words in American English that come from French and Spanish. ______________________

____

____

2. You need to gather your classmates to put on a play. ____________

____

3. You need to write a report about a local election for mayor.

____

____

4. You need to draw a map of Canada. ______________________

____

____

5. You want to find out about the weather in the Philippine Islands.

____

____

At Home: Have students choose a subject and tell where they would look for information.

Name ______________________ Date ____________ Practice 218

Form Generalizations

A **generalization** is a broad statement that is based on examples.

Read the following generalizations that were made based on "The Koala Catchers." Write two examples or facts from the selection that support each generalization.

Generalization: Koala bears are difficult to capture.

1. ______________________________

2. ______________________________

Generalization: Some people try to rescue koala bears.

3. ______________________________

____

4. ______________________________

____

Generalization: You will never find a koala bear living on the ground.

5. ______________________________

____

6. ______________________________

____

Generalization: Baby koalas stay close to their mothers.

7. ______________________________

____

8. ______________________________

____

At Home: Ask students to make a generalization about the importance of rescuing koala bears based on the information in "The Koala Catchers."

Name______________________ Date__________ Practice 219

Context Clues

When you find an unfamiliar word, read the words and sentences around it. They often can help you figure out the word's meaning.

Look at the word in dark type in each sentence. Underline the clues that help you figure out the word's meaning. Then mark an **X** next to the meaning of the word in dark type.

1. We flew to Mexico on an **airplane**. It took much less time than a train would have.

   _____ **a.** a flying machine _____ **b.** a bell

   _____ **c.** a person who acts _____ **d.** a helper

2. It's hard to **decide** what to do. I just can't make up my mind.

   _____ **a.** to pay someone _____ **b.** to take

   _____ **c.** to refuse _____ **d.** to make up one's mind

3. My mother said, "It's six o'clock—almost **dinnertime**. We're having chicken."

   _____ **a.** part of a person's face _____ **b.** a large balloon

   _____ **c.** a time when people eat dinner _____ **d.** a dinner plate

4. We heard a loud **crash**. A tree had fallen outside.

   _____ **a.** a break _____ **b.** a small bow

   _____ **c.** a small water animal _____ **d.** a loud noise

5. I call my **dentist** when my tooth hurts.

   _____ **a.** someone who cuts wood _____ **b.** someone who fixes teeth

   _____ **c.** someone who bakes bread _____ **d.** someone who cuts hair

At Home: Have students write a short story using the new words above.

Multiple-Meaning Words

When you come across a **multiple-meaning word**, use the words and sentences around it to understand its meaning.

The words in dark type below have more than one meaning. Use **context clues** to help you choose a word or phrase from the box that means the same as the word in dark type. Then write the word or phrase on the line after each sentence.

look at	something that can be heard
a line of railroad cars	make a picture of something
choose	a piece of metal that fits in a lock
cause	a small river

1. I used my **key** to open the door. ____________
2. Did you hear that loud **sound**? ____________
3. I like to **draw** my cat. ____________
4. Did you **see** the beautiful paintings? ____________
5. We took the **train** to Florida. ____________
6. He will **pick out** a new game at the store. ____________
7. She will **make** her bicycle move more slowly. ____________
8. The **stream** was shallow; it hadn't rained in a long time. ____________

At Home: Have students write sentences using the other meaning of each multiple-meaning word.

Name ______________________ Date ____________

Unit 3 Vocabulary Review

A. Supply the correct word from the box.

mistakes	perform	talented	brain	subject	conversation	boasting

One day Brian and Jill had a ____________________. This is what they said.

Brian: Sam is always ____________________.

Jill: Yes, I know. He says he has the best ____________________ in the class.

Brian: But he's not good in every ____________________. I'm better in science.

Jill: Yes. He makes ____________________ like the rest of us.

Brian: Even if he is ____________________, he doesn't have to ____________________ all the time.

B. Put an **X** next to the word you could use in place of the underlined vocabulary word.

1. It felt snug under the covers.

   a. safe ________ **b.** warm ________ **c.** cozy ________

2. A fast twist sent the top whirling.

   a. running ________ **b.** spinning ________ **c.** flying ________

3. Heather seized the dog's ball and threw it again.

   a. grabbed ________ **b.** tossed ________ **c.** bounced ________

10

At Home: Have students write a conversation like the one in Part A. They should use at least four vocabulary words in their conversation.

Name ______________________ Date ______________ **Practice 222**

Unit 3 Vocabulary Review

A. Supply the correct word from the box.

equipment	bitter	invisible	considering	crates	communicate

1. The juice tasted ______________ to Nobu.
2. Ms. Warner packed her dishes in ______________.
3. People can talk and ______________ by using their hands.
4. She was ______________ which book to buy.
5. You need lots of ______________ to play hockey.
6. Katy pretended to have an ______________ dog.

B. Read each definition. Choose a word from the box and write it on the line.

social	rescuers	hesitated	boasting

1. animals that live in groups ______________
2. waited before you acted ______________
3. people who save animals ______________
4. telling how great you are ______________

At Home: Have students write a sentence for each vocabulary word in Part B.

/10